To Cassandra

Happy Birthday!

Love from
    Chris, Rich, Nathan
        and Katrina

The Book of
NATURAL HISTORY

CONTENTS

This edition produced in 1994 for
Shooting Star Press Inc
230 Fifth Avenue
Suite 1212
New York, NY 10001

© Aladdin Books Ltd 1994

Designed and produced by
Aladdin Books Ltd
28 Percy Street
London W1

Writers: Lionel Bender, Linda Gamlin
Illustrators: Ron Hayward Associates
               Aziz A. Khan

All rights reserved
Printed in the Czech Republic
ISBN 1-56924-068-X

*Some of the material in this book was previously published in
the Today's World series*

The Book of
NATURAL
HISTORY

Written by Lionel Bender and Linda Gamlin
Illustrated by Ron Hayward Associates and Aziz A. Khan

INTRODUCTION

Life can be found everywhere on Earth. Plants, animals and man survive and thrive in the great variety of living conditions and extremes of climate which the Earth offers. Different species make the most of these conditions from ice-capped mountains, to forest and plain, desert, ocean and volcano. Animals adapt in amazing ways; there are snakes that fly; fish which walk or lay eggs on leaves in mid-air; flightless birds that graze like deer; and bears which grow hair on the soles of their feet.

Plants and animals have developed over billions of years, since the first living things evolved, probably in the sea. They were very simple, single-celled organisms. Gradually they developed into larger, more complex plants and animals. There have been many stages of evolution, but some of the main groups of animals that have emerged are insects, fish, amphibians, reptiles, birds and mammals. Mammals are the most highly evolved animals on Earth today. Humans are members of the mammal group.

A vast number of living things exist on Earth today. Scientists believe there are more than 350,000 species of plants, but no one knows for sure. Some are tiny; some are huge, like the giant sequoia trees of California (USA) (290 feet high and 30 feet wide) which are the largest living things on

Earth. Over a million kinds of animals have been classified, but each year, hundreds of new kinds are discovered. They range from microscopic forms to the largest animal which is the blue whale. It is longer than eight elephants in a row.

Every living thing fits into a marvellous system of nature. Without plants there would be no life at all, because the oxygen that we breathe comes from plants. Animals and plants depend on each other for food. Animals both provide food, and destroy life by hunting and killing other living things, but this helps to balance the total number of animals and plants on Earth. People not only depend on plants and animals for food, but also for materials for clothing, shelter and medicines. In addition plants and animals add beauty and pleasure to our lives.

Using photographs and diagrams, this book looks at the main groups of species living today, examining their structure, living conditions, feeding and reproduction processes, and their role in nature. Easy-to-follow classification tables and evolutionary and extinction charts are provided at the back, for quick reference, as well as a detailed glossary and index.

PLANTS

CONTENTS

INTRODUCTION

There are two main types of living things on Earth – animals and plants. The main biological differences between the two are the way they feed and the fact that most animals can move around whereas nearly all plants remain in one place. Animals drink water and eat plants or other animals to get the raw materials they need to function and grow. They breathe in oxygen from the air and breathe our carbon dioxide as a waste product. They also have nerves and specialized sense organs such as eyes and ears.

   Plants also take in water (from the soil) but manufacture most of their own food by the process of photosynthesis. This uses the energy of sunlight to combine carbon dioxide gas from the air with water to make sugars, at the same time releasing oxygen. It is brought about by the substance chlorophyll, a pigment which is responsible for the green color of most plants. Like animals, plants are made up of cells but these have rigid walls which provide support. And unlike animals, plants have no sense organs or a nervous system. A very few plants have adapted to trap insects, which they use as a source of food and minerals.

Major types:

Bacteria are single-celled organisms, often classed as neither plant nor animal because the cell structure is simple and not all bacteria make use of photosynthesis. Single-celled true plants include pond organisms such as Euglena. These can photosynthesize but also, like animal cells, break down complex food material.

Viruses are regarded as the link between living and non-living forms.

The simplest plants consist of a single cell, with a thin skin-like covering or membrane and a complex mixture of chemicals inside. Among these chemicals is chlorophyll, a green pigment that can trap the energy of sunlight and use it to power chemical reactions within the cell. Some bacteria are single-celled organisms of this type. Other primitive plants, such as water plants that resemble bundles of green hair, are made up of thread-like chains of cells. Next on the scale of complexity are seaweeds and mosses, which also have simple chains of cells in their multicellular bodies. Groups of specially modified cells carry the plants' reproductive organs. At a slightly higher level still are ferns, which grow leafy fronds. The fronds have areas on their undersides which carry spores, from which the plants reproduce.

PLANT CELL
(× 750)

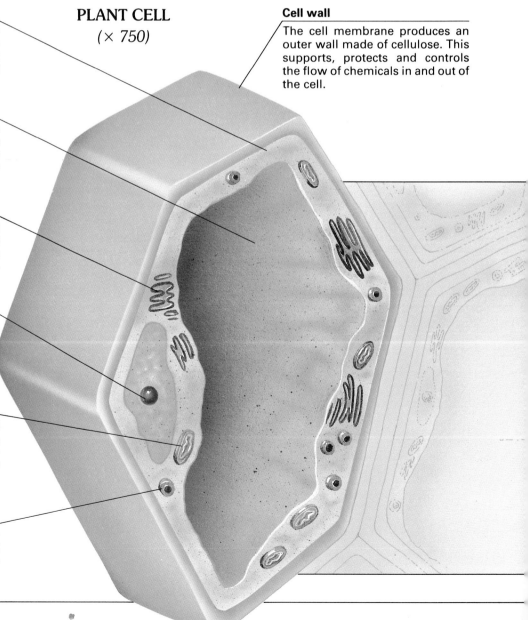

Membrane and cytoplasm

A thin membrane encloses the jelly-like contents of the cell (cytoplasm), in which are embedded all the working parts of the cell called the organelles.

Vacuole

At the center of the cell is a space filled with water, the vacuole. This enlarges as the plant takes up water, and gets smaller in dry conditions.

Endoplasmic reticulum

This system of fine tubes running through the cytoplasm allows the movement of chemicals between the nucleus and the cell membrane.

Nucleus

The control center of the cell. It is enclosed within a membrane and contains the genetic material that directs the cell's actions.

Mitochondrion

One of many energy-producing centers within the cytoplasm. Mitochondria are usually oval-shaped and are often called the cell's powerhouses.

Chloroplast

Similar to mitochondria, chloroplasts contain the green pigment chlorophyll, which traps the energy of sunlight to make sugars.

Cell wall

The cell membrane produces an outer wall made of cellulose. This supports, protects and controls the flow of chemicals in and out of the cell.

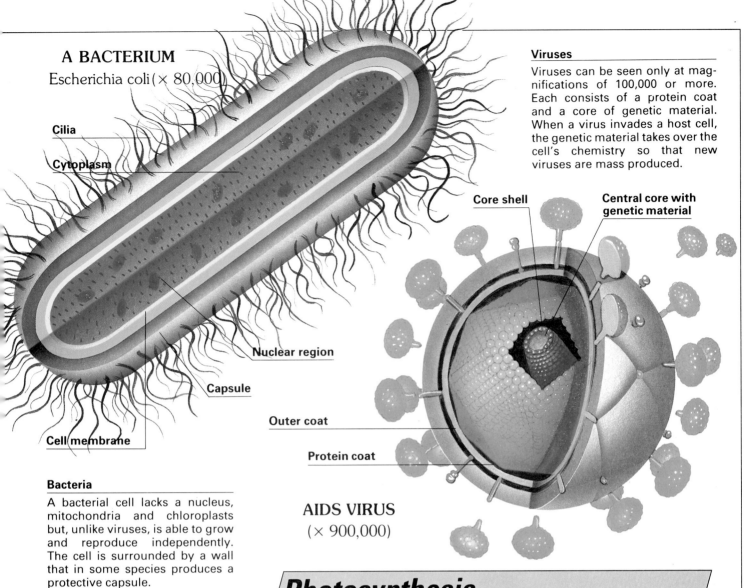

A BACTERIUM
Escherichia coli ($\times$ 80,000)

Cilia

Cytoplasm

Nuclear region

Capsule

Cell membrane

Viruses
Viruses can be seen only at magnifications of 100,000 or more. Each consists of a protein coat and a core of genetic material. When a virus invades a host cell, the genetic material takes over the cell's chemistry so that new viruses are mass produced.

Core shell

Central core with genetic material

Outer coat

Protein coat

AIDS VIRUS
($\times$ 900,000)

Bacteria
A bacterial cell lacks a nucleus, mitochondria and chloroplasts but, unlike viruses, is able to grow and reproduce independently. The cell is surrounded by a wall that in some species produces a protective capsule.

Photosynthesis

Cells cannot live without energy, food, water and oxygen. Animal cells feed on plant or animal material and break down the large, complex chemicals within this to obtain essential nutrients and energy. Oxygen and water pass into the cells from the surroundings. Plant cells, by contrast, use the energy of sunlight to convert carbon dioxide and water into sugars, which is the function of photosynthesis. They then convert the sugars into other nutrients or break them down to release energy. A typical flowering plant, from a grass to an oak tree, takes up water and mineral salts from the soil through its roots. Carbon dioxide enters the leaves through tiny holes in the leaf surface. In sunlight, sugars are made and oxygen is formed, which then passes out of the plant's leaves. At night, the plant uses oxygen to break down the sugars.

Sun

Oxygen

Energy

Carbohydrates (sugars)

Carbon dioxide

Water and minerals

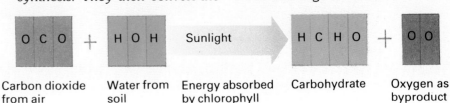

| O C O | + | H O H | Sunlight | H C H O | + | O O |

Carbon dioxide from air

Water from soil

Energy absorbed by chlorophyll

Carbohydrate

Oxygen as byproduct

ALGAE

There are about 20,000 species of algae, found in fresh water and seas throughout the world. They include green algae, such as the common hair-like pond plant called Spirogyra and the "leafy" sea lettuce Ulva, and the red and brown algae, common as seashore seaweeds such as bladderwrack, oar weed and dulse.

Algae range in size and form from microscopic single-celled plants that live on damp rocks or corals to the multicellular 60 m (200 feet) long strap-like seaweeds such as kelp, which are found off the coasts of California. They contain one or more types of pigment and obtain energy by photosynthesis. They are simple in structure. Blue-green algae are microscopic plants that resemble bacteria, and even the largest of seaweeds lack distinct roots, stems and leaves. Most algae are aquatic and are found in ponds, lakes and seas, where they sometimes multiply so rapidly that they color the water green or – in species with a red pigment – pink or orange.

Single or groups

Two types of single-celled algae-like species are the diatoms and desmids. Diatoms have shell-like cases made of silica, the chemical of sand, and consist of two sections. Some diatoms are circular and resemble a hat box with a base and a lid. Others are sausage-, oval- or S-shaped. Desmids also have a cell in two sections, but instead of a silica shell have a cellulose cell wall, as in more complex plants. The pond alga Spirogyra is made up of a string, or filament, of identical cells. Among seaweeds, the common feathery green and red types consist of highly branched filaments joined together, whereas kelps are composed of various types of cells arranged in groups to form leaf-like fronds.

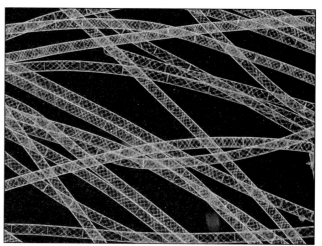

Spirogyra consists of hair-like filaments.

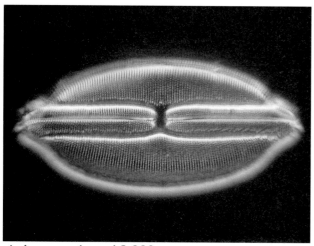

A diatom enlarged 2,000 times

Green, brown and red seaweeds at low tide

Reproduction

Some microscopic seaweeds are able to reproduce by breaking up into parts. Blue-green algae and some single-celled green algae reproduce by forming buds that split off or by growth and division of the cell in two. Colonies of such species as Volvox result from repeated cell divisions and are held together by a slimy sheath. The freshwater and seawater green alga called Chlamydomonas can reproduce both sexually and asexually. A single cell can divide into two identical daughter cells (asexually) or, as shown below, give rise to the equivalent of male and female sex cells, or gametes. Gametes from different plants fuse to form first a zygote and then a zygospore, which has a thick protective cell wall. The zygospore later germinates into four new cells.

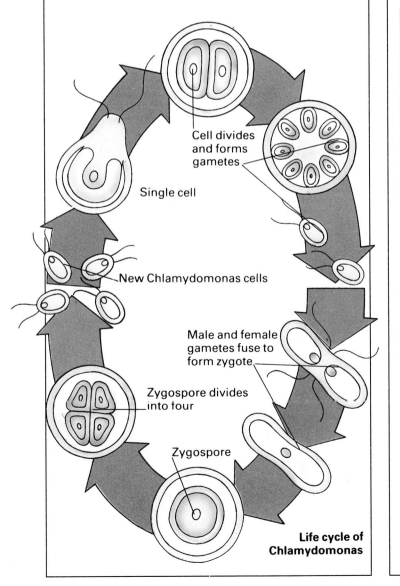

Cell divides and forms gametes

Single cell

New Chlamydomonas cells

Male and female gametes fuse to form zygote

Zygospore divides into four

Zygospore

Life cycle of Chlamydomonas

Life style

Large seaweeds of the seashore and coastal waters are usually attached to rocks by means of a special base, called the holdfast. Their long, flat fronds wave about in the water currents. In spring, swellings appear on the tips of fronds and shed male and female gametes into the water. The gametes fuse and produce zygospores that later develop into new plants. Blue-green and other single-celled algae are found in most damp, warm habitats where there is adequate light. Some live inside flatworms that burrow in sand as the tide comes in and move to the surface as the tide ebbs. The algae provide the worms with food in the form of sugars made by photosynthesis. The algae need sunlight for this, which is provided as the flatworms migrate to the surface when there is no danger.

The largest seaweeds are called kelp.

Flatworms colored green by the algae

FUNGI

Major types:
"Imperfect" fungi reproduce only by asexual means, e.g. ringworm fungus. **Phycomycetes** (2,000 species) reproduce sexually but do not form complex fruiting bodies, e.g. bread molds. **Ascomycetes** (70,000) sexually produce sac-like cells, e.g. yeasts and cup fungi. **Basidiomycetes** (30,000) sexually produce spores, e.g. mushrooms, toadstools and puffballs.

Fungi are often classified separately from other plants because they lack chlorophyll and most have a simple cell structure. Many live as saprophytes, dissolving dead or decaying animal and plant matter and feeding on the nutrient-rich liquid. There are more than 100,000 species of fungi, ranging from single-celled yeasts to multicellular mushrooms and toadstools. Fungi inhabit nearly every environment where life is possible. They are chief enemies of larger plants and some cause human diseases – for example, ringworm. However, some molds produce chemicals used as antibiotic drugs. And yeasts make bread dough rise and bring about the fermentation used to make alcohol in wine and beer.

Structure

Yeasts are single cells that are often enclosed in a slimy capsule, and have a well-defined nucleus and a cell wall made of various sugars. Another group of fungi, the molds, rusts and smuts, are made up of a network of narrow tubular branches called hyphae. These are the feeding structures common to all large fungi. Hyphae consist of yeast-like cells fused together to form a hollow cylinder. In toadstools and mushrooms the network of hyphae is underground. The toadstools and mushrooms that we see, are fruiting bodies that produce spores.

Clusters of spore on a microscopic mold

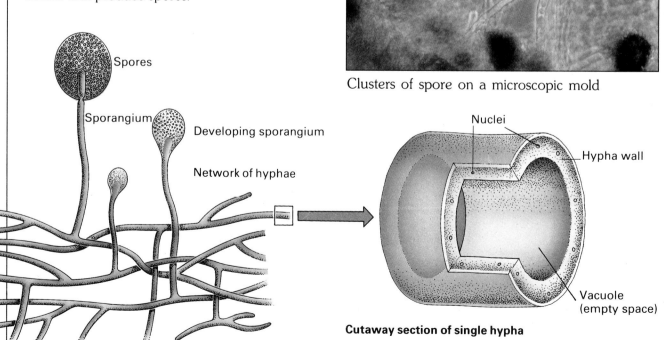

Spores

Sporangium

Developing sporangium

Network of hyphae

Nuclei

Hypha wall

Vacuole (empty space)

Cutaway section of single hypha

Feeding

The common bread mold and similar fungi live on rotting vegetation or on fruit. They produce hair-like hyphae that penetrate the food source in the same way that the roots of other plants spread through the soil. Cells of the hyphae release chemicals known as enzymes. These break down complex substances such as proteins, fats and sugars into simpler ones which, along with water and vital mineral salts, readily pass into the hyphae.

A bracket fungus growing on a tree trunk

Reproduction

Most fungi reproduce by forming spores. When a spore lands on a suitable material it sprouts, producing a network of hyphae. This produces fruiting bodies which, in mushrooms and toadstools, consists of an "umbrella" with gills densely covered with spore-producing structures. The spores are shot out of the gills and carried away by the wind. Stinkhorns produce spores that are dispersed when they stick to the bodies of insects, such as flies.

A puffball releasing a cloud of spores

Partnerships

Lichens are primitive plants formed by the partnership of a fungus and an alga. The fungus makes up the main body of the plant, providing a home for groups of cells of the alga. In return, the alga uses photosynthesis to make sugars that the fungus absorbs as food. The combined organism grows more slowly and is more resilient and adaptable than either partner. There are more than 15,000 species of lichen. They are found on rocks, buildings and tree trunks, and range in size from that of a pinhead to leafy structures 2m (7ft) across. Some produce antibiotic drugs effective against diseases such as pneumonia. One, Cladonia rangiferina, is called reindeer moss because it is the main food of reindeer during the Arctic winter, when there is little other plant food.

Reindeer feeding on reindeer moss (a lichen)

MOSSES AND LIVERWORTS

Mosses: about 14,000 species including the bog mosses Sphagnum. **Liverworts:** 9,000 species, each with a flattened appearance. **Hornworts:** about 100 species that resemble liverworts but have a different type of spore-producing capsule.

Growing as a blanket-like covering on ponds, river banks and the floors of damp woods, or as the mat of vegetation forming bogs, mosses and liverworts are the simplest and most primitive of land plants. Although similar to seaweeds, with a compact body many cells thick and a method of sexual reproduction dependent on water, their cell structure is like that of more highly evolved plants with an outer layer (the epidermis) that prevents them from drying out. Most mosses, liverworts and the related hornworts are small green plants. They grow best in warm moist climates and most species are found in the tropics, growing on tree trunks or on the forest floor.

Life cycle

As an adaptation to living on land, mosses and liverworts have a complex life cycle involving two distinct stages. The first and main stage, called the gametophyte, depends on water for reproduction. The second stage, the sporophyte, produces microscopic spores that can survive periods of drought before germinating.

The gametophyte reproduces sexually, producing male and female organs called antheridia and archegonia. In mosses especially, these organs can be seen developing at the tips of the upright growing leaf shoots. They produce sex cells, or gametes: male spermatozoids and female ova. The spermatozoids must swim to the ova to fertilize them and, because the male and female organs may be on separate plants, this requires the surface of the plants to be covered in water. On land this occurs along river banks, when it rains or when there is a heavy dew. The fertilized ova develop into spore-producing forms, the sporophytes. These grow as parasites on the mature plant, absorbing food from its leaves. They send up an aerial shoot with a capsule at the tip that produces thousands of spores. The spores are carried away by the wind. When they reach a suitable habitat, each spore sprouts and forms a young shoot, called the protonema. This develops underground roots and an aerial shoot, and eventually forms a new gametophyte plant.

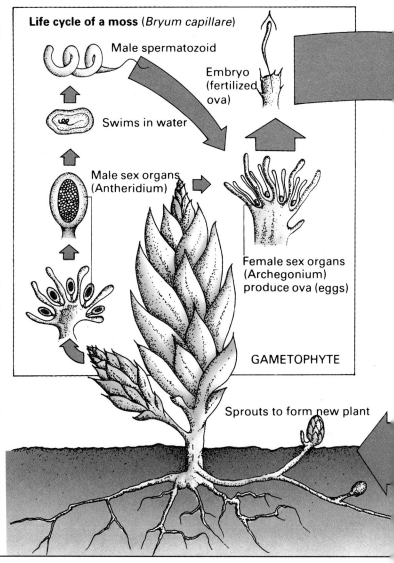

Life cycle of a moss (*Bryum capillare*)

Male spermatozoid

Swims in water

Embryo (fertilized ova)

Male sex organs (Antheridium)

Female sex organs (Archegonium) produce ova (eggs)

GAMETOPHYTE

Sprouts to form new plant

Star-shaped female sex organs of a liverwort

Shape and form

The main body of common liverworts such as Marchantia and Conocephalum, which grow on river banks throughout the world, and of hornworts, is a plate-like structure often resembling the lobes of a liver. This is why (and because they were once used to treat diseases of the liver) they are called liverworts. Leafy liverworts, such as Pleurozia in peat bogs, have branched creeping stems clothed with tiny leaves. Mosses have a similar form but the stems grow more upright and the leaves are largely made up of hollow cells with small pores in their walls so that they absorb and store large amounts of water. Mosses such as Sphagnum grow in dense masses, their lower parts decaying slowly to form peat.

Sporophyte grows on gametophyte plant

Capsule

SPOROPHYTE

Spores blown by wind

Protonema

A close-up of Sphagnum moss

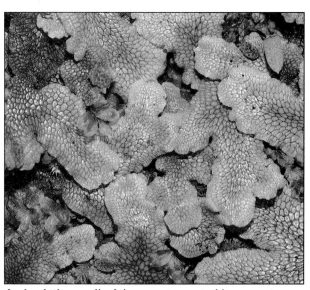

Lobed "leaves" of the great scented liverwort

FERNS

Ferns (about 100,000 species) produce spores in stalked spore cases that grow in clusters under mature leaves. **Horsetails** (30) produce spores in cones and manufacture most food in their ridged stem. **Clubmosses** (1,250) are small and moss-like and produce spores in club-like cones. All three types grow in greatest numbers and diversity in rain forests of Southeast Asia.

Ferns are leafy plants which, in complexity, lie between primitive and highly evolved plants. Like algae, mosses and liverworts they have a life cycle with two forms, are spread by spores, and are dependent on water for male sex cells to swim to the female cells. But like cone- and seed-bearing plants, they have a main body divided into roots, stems and leaves and a network of tubes, the vascular system, that links these and permits movement of food and water to all parts of the plant. Horsetails and clubmosses resemble ferns in structure and partly in life style, but their leaves are minute and scale-like and the spore-bearing tissues are grouped into cones.

Structure

Horsetails have an upright stem, sprays of green branches and small scale-like leaves. Clubmosses usually have tufts of branching stems covered with tiny leaves. Ferns grow as shrubs, creeping vine-like plants, or even as trees. All three types have a vascular system in which elongated cells are grouped and linked together to form either parallel columns or a meshwork (lattice) of conducting tissue. The vascular system extends from the tips of water-absorbing roots into the food-producing leaves. In ferns especially, the cells of the system are rigid and provide support for the plants.

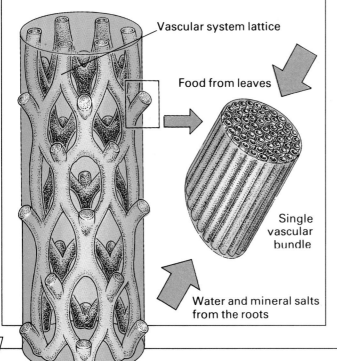

Vascular system lattice

Food from leaves

Single vascular bundle

Water and mineral salts from the roots

Shape and form

Roots anchor ferns to the soil, allowing them to grow upright stems bearing many leaves, and some ferns reach tree-like proportions. True tree ferns are tropical species with trunks built up of leaf bases, as in palm trees. They can grow to 21m (70ft) tall. Bracken is a fern often regarded as a weed because it thrives on pasture land. Horsetails vary from small creeping plants to scramblers reaching 9m (30ft) across. Clubmosses once included giant tree forms that were buried in bogs millions of years ago and formed into coal, but most present-day species are only small plants.

Spore-bearing cones of a horsetail

Life cycle

Among ferns, the dominant form is the spore-producing plant or sporophyte. This consists of a short stem, the rhizome, from which roots grow down into the soil, and leaves or fronds, which grow upward. On the underside of mature fronds spore cases (called sori) develop. Each contains several stalked capsules, the sporangia, which as they ripen burst and shed their spores into the air. When spores land on moist soil, they germinate and produce a small leaf-like plant, the gametophyte. This bears male and female organs containing microscopic sperm and ova. After fertilization, the ova develop into new sporophytes.

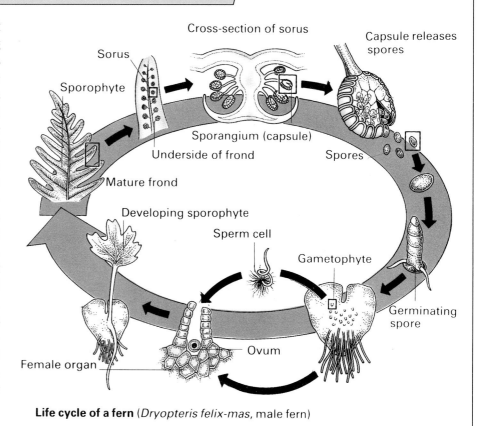

Life cycle of a fern (*Dryopteris felix-mas*, male fern)

Lower plants chart

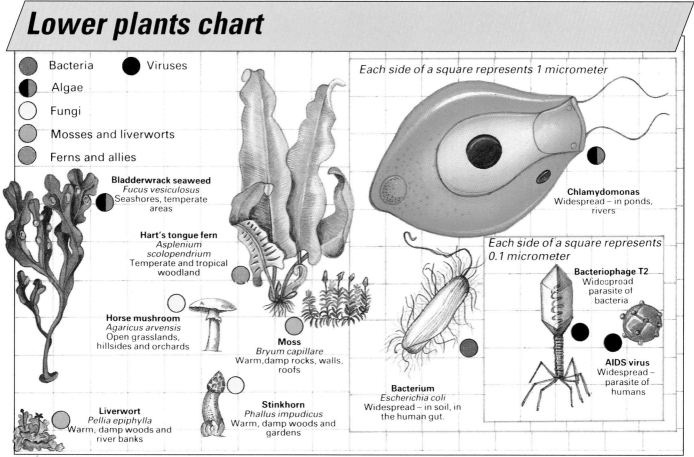

● Bacteria ● Viruses
◐ Algae
○ Fungi
◔ Mosses and liverworts
◑ Ferns and allies

Bladderwrack seaweed
Fucus vesiculosus
Seashores, temperate areas

Hart's tongue fern
Asplenium scolopendrium
Temperate and tropical woodland

Horse mushroom
Agaricus arvensis
Open grasslands, hillsides and orchards

Moss
Bryum capillare
Warm, damp rocks, walls, roofs

Liverwort
Pellia epiphylla
Warm, damp woods and river banks

Stinkhorn
Phallus impudicus
Warm, damp woods and gardens

Bacterium
Escherichia coli
Widespread – in soil, in the human gut.

Each side of a square represents 1 micrometer

Chlamydomonas
Widespread – in ponds, rivers

Each side of a square represents 0.1 micrometer

Bacteriophage T2
Widespread parasite of bacteria

AIDS virus
Widespread – parasite of humans

Each side of a square represents 10cm

CONE-BEARING PLANTS

Cone-bearing trees, like all flowering plants, have evolved two unique reproductive structures: the pollen grain and the seed. Their sexual reproduction is no longer dependent on a watery environment and so they have colonized all land areas. Pollen grains, the male sex cells, are tiny and encased in a protective waterproof wrapping so they can be spread by wind or insects. Seeds are essentially female gametophytes that remain on the main plant, the sporophyte, in order to build up a food store and take on the task of dispersal. Conifers and their allies bear small pollen-bearing male cones and larger seed-bearing female cones. Most are evergreen trees with needle-shaped leaves.

Major types:

Conifers (about 500 species) include pine, larch, spruce and fir trees. Occur mainly in cool, temperate climates.

Cycads (about 50) are sparsely but widely distributed throughout the tropics and the Southern Hemisphere.

Ginkgo, or maidenhair tree, has leaves like the maidenhair fern.

Yews (9) have female cones that resemble fleshy fruits.

Gnetales (2) include the twitch plants and the Kalahari Desert plant Welwitschia.

The softwood trunk

At the center of a conifer trunk lies the heartwood, which is made up of dead cells. Sapwood comprises rings of food-transporting vessels, a new ring being laid down each year by the cambium layer of cells. The protective bark has a dead outer layer and a spongy, growing inner layer. As a group, conifers are known as softwoods.

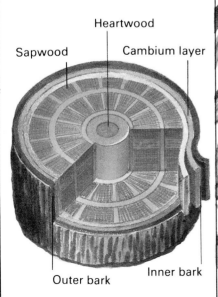

Heartwood

Sapwood   Cambium layer

Outer bark   Inner bark

Cones

Conifers bear separate male and female catkin-like cones which bear male and female scales. The female cones, after fertilization of the ova, enlarge, turn green, then become woody and brown.

Leaves

These are usually long, narrow and needle-like, which reduces water loss so that the trees can keep their leaves in winter. Larches, though, lose their leaves each autumn.

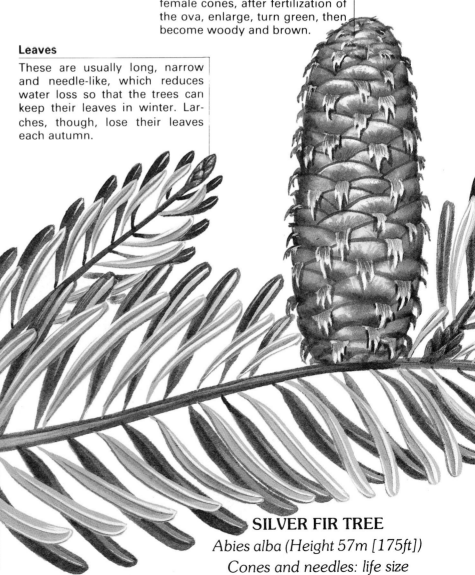

SILVER FIR TREE
Abies alba (Height 57m [175ft])
Cones and needles: life size

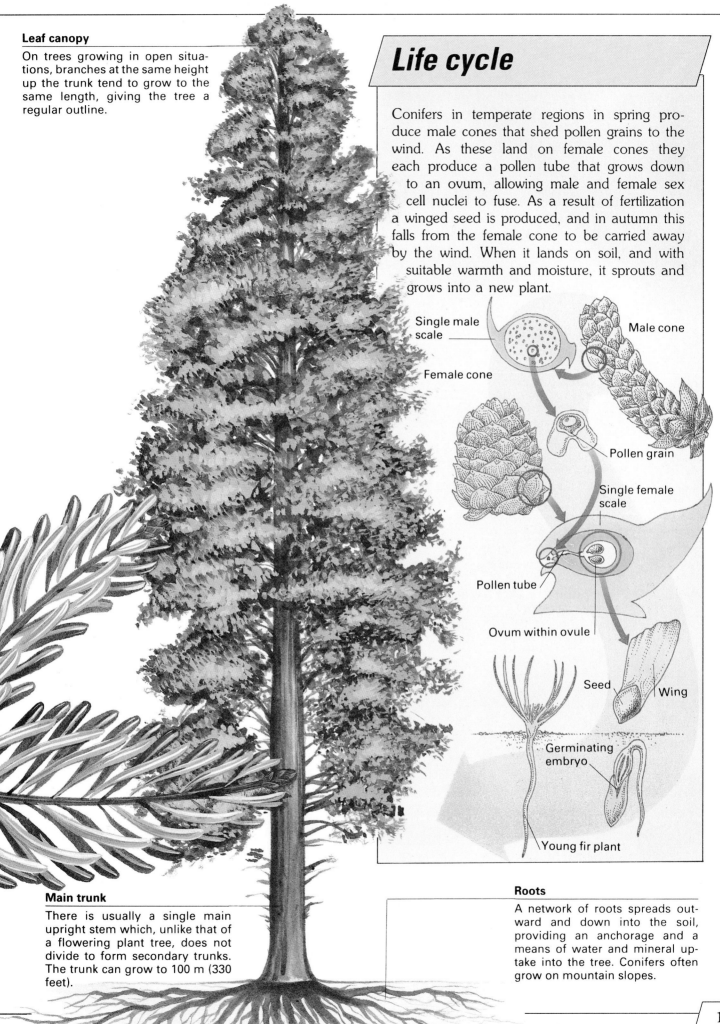

Leaf canopy

On trees growing in open situations, branches at the same height up the trunk tend to grow to the same length, giving the tree a regular outline.

Life cycle

Conifers in temperate regions in spring produce male cones that shed pollen grains to the wind. As these land on female cones they each produce a pollen tube that grows down to an ovum, allowing male and female sex cell nuclei to fuse. As a result of fertilization a winged seed is produced, and in autumn this falls from the female cone to be carried away by the wind. When it lands on soil, and with suitable warmth and moisture, it sprouts and grows into a new plant.

Single male scale

Male cone

Female cone

Pollen grain

Single female scale

Pollen tube

Ovum within ovule

Seed

Wing

Germinating embryo

Young fir plant

Main trunk

There is usually a single main upright stem which, unlike that of a flowering plant tree, does not divide to form secondary trunks. The trunk can grow to 100 m (330 feet).

Roots

A network of roots spreads outward and down into the soil, providing an anchorage and a means of water and mineral uptake into the tree. Conifers often grow on mountain slopes.

Trunk

About 230 million years ago conifer trees dominated the Earth's plants, forming a thick belt of forest over much of the land. Today relatively few types remain, but of these the North American Douglas fir, giant sequoia and California redwoods are the tallest trees in the world, standing up to 115m (385 feet) tall and with a distance around the base of the trunk of 14m (46 feet). Yews are among the slowest growing trees. Plants in the Arctic regions along the edge of the forest belt can take tens of years to grow just a few inches in height. The trunk wood of conifers is soft and contains chemicals known as resins. These give freshly cut softwood a characteristic smell of turpentine. In cross-section the wood differs from that of flowering plant trees in that lengthwise water-containing vessels are absent. In the north of America, Europe and Asia conifer trees are often grown in huge plantations as a source of commercial wood. When the trees are fully grown they are cut down and transport to lumberyards. Here the softwood is used as timber for building, to make plywood or chipboard, or pulp for paper.

Logs can be burned as fuel.

Sequoia, the world's largest tree

Leaves

Fir trees bear evergreen leaves or needles in groups of two to five at regular intervals along the stems. Larches have deciduous leaves or needles similarly arranged but in clusters of ten or more. Cypress trees are Northern Hemisphere conifers with evergreen scale-like leaves pressed closely against the stems. Pine trees are the most familiar conifer in North America.

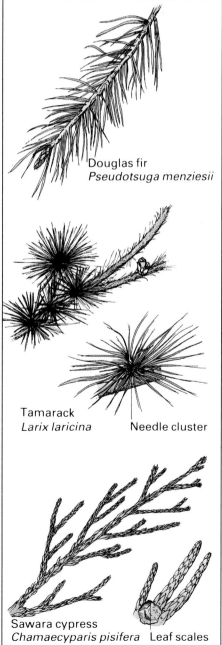

Douglas fir
Pseudotsuga menziesii

Tamarack
Larix laricina   Needle cluster

Sawara cypress
Chamaecyparis pisifera   Leaf scales

Cones

Conifers are often called gymnosperms (meaning naked seeds) because the ovules – ova-containing structures – are borne directly on special leaves, the scales, and not enclosed in an ovary as in flowering plants. The scales are grouped together to form cones. Cones are either male or female. In many species the sexes are on different trees, but in the larger conifers there are often male and female cones on the same shoots. Yews produce single ovules not on scales like true conifers but surrounded by a fleshy berry-like aril. The cones of cycads can grow to 60 cm (2 feet) and weigh 25 kg (55 lb).

The cone of a rare cycad

"Cones" of yews look like berries.

Cone-bearing plants chart

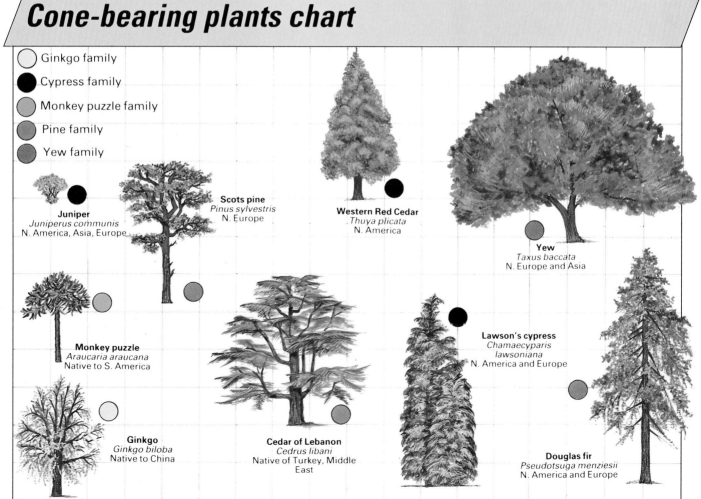

○ Ginkgo family
● Cypress family
○ Monkey puzzle family
○ Pine family
○ Yew family

Juniper
Juniperus communis
N. America, Asia, Europe

Scots pine
Pinus sylvestris
N. Europe

Western Red Cedar
.*Thuya plicata*
N. America

Yew
Taxus baccata
N. Europe and Asia

Monkey puzzle
Araucaria araucana
Native to S. America

Lawson's cypress
Chamaecyparis lawsoniana
N. America and Europe

Ginkgo
Ginkgo biloba
Native to China

Cedar of Lebanon
Cedrus libani
Native of Turkey, Middle East

Douglas fir
Pseudotsuga menziesii
N. America and Europe

Each side of a square represents 10m (30 feet)

FLOWERING PLANTS

Two main types:
Monocots have only one leaf-like organ, or cotyledon, within the seed. They include grasses, palms and orchids (55,000 species). They have narrow leaves and the petals of the flowers arranged in threes or sixes. **Dicots** have two cotyledons within the seed. They include woody trees and shrubs and many plants grown for food and garden decoration (200,000 species). They have a variety of leaf shapes and flowers with petals usually arranged in fours or fives.

More than 80 per cent of all living green plants – some 255,000 species – are flowering plants. They are the dominant group of land plants in the world today and include most trees, all grasses, herbs, carnivorous plants and many aquatic plants. They differ from other seed-bearing plants such as conifers in usually having flowers, seeds enclosed in fruits, and a well-developed food- and water-conducting system. Flowers bear pollen-producing male organs and egg cells that form the female ovule. They encourage transfer of pollen from flower to flower – pollination – by insects and other animals. Flowering plants are also known as angiosperms (meaning covered seeds). This refers to a layer of tissue called the carpel, which encloses the seed and later forms a fruit which aids the seed's dispersal.

Life cycle

Flowers are concerned with sexual reproduction. The male parts are the stamens, and the female parts consist of a pollen-receiving stigma and an ovary, which bears the embryo seed or ovule. Pollen grains are carried to the stigma by the wind or by insects such as bees and flies. There the pollen grain produces a pollen tube that penetrates the ovule. Pollen and ovule cell nuclei fuse and produce an embryo. As the embryo develops, the carpel forms a food store, the endosperm, and a seed coat, the testa. The seed ripens and the stamens, petals and sepals fall off to leave a fruit. The fruit is carried by the wind or by an animal. Given warmth and moisture, the seed germinates to produce first a small root, then a leaf shoot. The cotyledons provide food for the young plant and protect the first true leaves.

POLLINATION
Stigma
Pollen
Ovary
Stamen
Sepal
Pollen tube
Stigma
Egg nucleus
Ovule
Growing point
FERTILIZATION
Embryo
First true leaves
Cotyledons
Endosperm
Radicle
Testa
Roots
GERMINATION

LIFE CYCLE OF A DICOT

MEADOW BUTTERCUP
Ranunculus acris

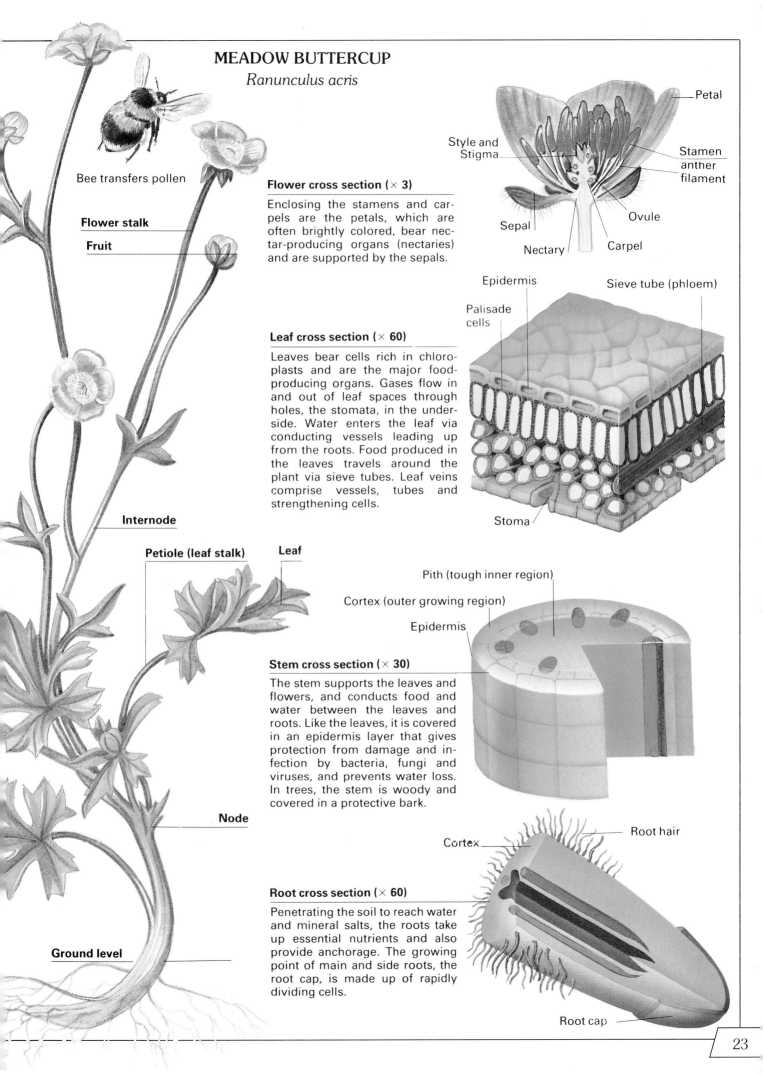

Bee transfers pollen

Flower stalk

Fruit

Internode

Petiole (leaf stalk)   **Leaf**

Node

Ground level

Style and Stigma

Sepal

Nectary

Petal

Stamen
anther
filament

Ovule

Carpel

Flower cross section (× 3)

Enclosing the stamens and carpels are the petals, which are often brightly colored, bear nectar-producing organs (nectaries) and are supported by the sepals.

Epidermis

Palisade cells

Sieve tube (phloem)

Stoma

Leaf cross section (× 60)

Leaves bear cells rich in chloroplasts and are the major food-producing organs. Gases flow in and out of leaf spaces through holes, the stomata, in the underside. Water enters the leaf via conducting vessels leading up from the roots. Food produced in the leaves travels around the plant via sieve tubes. Leaf veins comprise vessels, tubes and strengthening cells.

Pith (tough inner region)

Cortex (outer growing region)

Epidermis

Stem cross section (× 30)

The stem supports the leaves and flowers, and conducts food and water between the leaves and roots. Like the leaves, it is covered in an epidermis layer that gives protection from damage and infection by bacteria, fungi and viruses, and prevents water loss. In trees, the stem is woody and covered in a protective bark.

Root hair

Cortex

Root cross section (× 60)

Penetrating the soil to reach water and mineral salts, the roots take up essential nutrients and also provide anchorage. The growing point of main and side roots, the root cap, is made up of rapidly dividing cells.

Root cap

The term shrub is used for woody plants that lack an obvious trunk but have a number of shoots rising up from the base. Temperate shrubs include hawthorn, hazel and birch. Temperate deciduous forest trees include oak, ash, beech and elm.

Temperate regions include much of North America, northern Eurasia and coastal regions of Australasia.

In temperate regions the climate tends to be warm or hot in summer and cold in winter. The marked cold season limits the type of flowering plants that can grow in these areas. Most trees that grow there shed their leaves in autumn to cope with the limited supply of water during the winter and to avoid frost damage. Within any one species, trees that grow in very cold areas – where conifers usually dominate – tend to be shorter and more shrub-like than those growing in warmer parts. The flowers of temperate trees and shrubs are mostly small and inconspicuous and are usually adapted for wind or wind and insect pollination, because there are fewer insects there than in the tropics.

Leaves and fruits

In spring, temperate trees and shrubs put on a growth spurt and develop new leaves and flowers. Throughout spring and summer the leaves photosynthesize and build up the plant's food reserves. A considerable amount of nutrients and energy is used to form seeds that will disperse the plant and to develop leaf buds for next year's growth. In autumn, deciduous trees shed all their leaves. Evergreen trees and shrubs, such as holly, shed their leaves in small numbers throughout the year. Cells at the base of the leaf stalk form a corky layer which stops the flow of water to the leaf. Eventually the leaf dies and falls off.

Holly is an evergreen shrub.

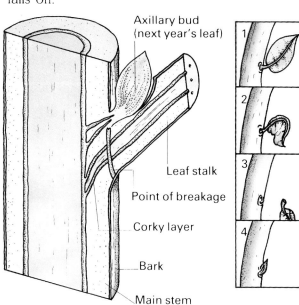
Axillary bud
(next year's leaf)

Leaf stalk

Point of breakage

Corky layer

Bark

Main stem

1
2
3
4

Acorns are the fruits of the oak tree.

Pollination

The transfer of pollen from male anthers to female stigma is called pollination. Catkins, the clusters of tiny flowers of trees such as hazel, use the wind for pollination. They are borne on stems before the leaves appear. Each flower produces a mass of light pollen grains that are easily shaken off by the slightest breeze. The stigma sticks out beyond the petals to catch any pollen that blows by. Most fruit trees, such as apples, have scented flowers that are attractive to insects. As an insect feeds on the pollen or nectar, it brushes against the anthers and pollen sticks to its hairs. When the insect visits another flower, the pollen brushes off on the stigma.

Pollen showers from hazel catkins

A bee transfers pollen on cherry blossom.

Yearly cycle

Deciduous trees, such as oak, horse chestnut and ash, change their appearance with the seasons. At the beginning of spring, branches and twigs are bare of leaves and flowers. By summer the tree is in full leaf and flowers have appeared. After pollination, seeds and fruits develop. With the onset of autumn, the leaves start to turn color and fall, and the fruits begin to be dispersed or are eaten by animals such as squirrels and birds. During winter, the tree is almost dormant. Buds are the only visible signs of life, but they do not open until spring. Many trees can live several hundred years, repeating this growth pattern with the endless cycle of the seasons.

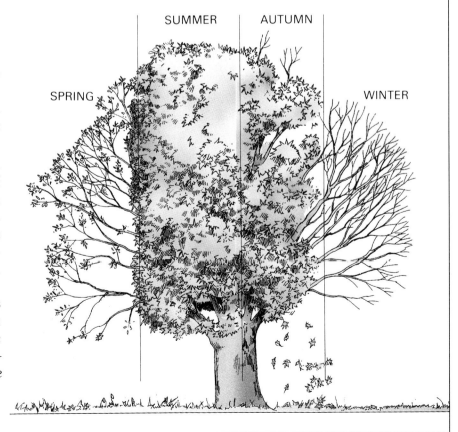

SPRING SUMMER AUTUMN WINTER

TREES AND SHRUBS (Tropical)

There are two major types:
Food trees and shrubs – species that produce leaves and fruits that are used for drinks and food – for example tea, coffee, cocoa, banana and date palm. **Timber trees and shrubs** – species that produce a tough wood, such as mahogany, teak and ebony.

The tropics – the world's perpetually hot climates – include most of central Africa, southern Asia, northern Australasia and northern South America. In the hottest and wettest regions, such as the Amazon River basin, many kinds of evergreen flowering plants thrive. The trees have a year-long growing season and form thick, lush rainforests, often called jungle. Where there is less rainfall and a distinct dry season each year, both deciduous and semi-evergreen trees grow. At the fringes of the tropics the dry season may last for many months. There most of the trees are deciduous and, like the acacias of the African savannah, are mostly flat-topped and widely scattered.

Shapes and sizes

Tropical rainforests contain the greatest diversity and number of flowering trees and shrubs. There are five zones of vegetation. The tallest trees grow to 60 m (200 feet) and produce a mass of branches, leaves and flowers – the crown – at the top of their trunk. The crowns stick up high above the rest of the forest, receiving the maximum of light. Below is the canopy, or forest roof, an interlocking mass of crowns of trees 15-30 m (50-100 ft) tall. Scattered below are trees up to 15 m (50 ft) tall with crowns shaped by the direction of light. At the lowest level are young trees and shrubs.

Tall trees that thrust their crowns high above the forest roof are known as emergents.

Broad crowns of closely packed trees form an almost unbroken sea of foliage 30 m (100 ft) above the forest floor.

Beneath the canopy trees compete for light. Their tops seem to stretch up in search of sunlight.

Sparse shrubs and young trees grow in the shadowy gloom of the other trees.

Ferns grow on the damp forest soil.

Tall trees in the Venezuelan rainforest

Trunk and leaves

With many tall tropical trees, the base of the trunk and roots form thick supporting buttresses. Higher up, the trunk and branches act as hosts for other flowering plants such as strangler figs. These grow from seeds that lodge in the host's bark and send down roots that surround and gradually decompose it. Trees of dry areas of the tropics, such as the baobab of Africa, have a small crown and a trunk that stores water to allow the plant to survive long periods of drought. The eucalyptus, or gum, trees of Australia produce evergreen water-retaining leaves of two types – rounded, stalkless young leaves and small, long and narrow, stalked adult ones.

A fat-trunked baobab tree in Kenya

Koalas feed on Australian eucalyptus trees.

Fruits

With constant sunshine and rain, tropical trees and shrubs can produce fruit all year round. The fruits are often large and colorful and have juicy, tasty centers – such as with bananas and mangos. This encourages animals to feed on them, and in this way the animals disperse the seeds that are inside the fruits. Many fruits of emergent trees are eaten by birds such as toucans and hornbills. Those of forest canopy trees form the diet of monkeys and apes, which are constantly on the move in search of trees in fruit. Trees that grow by the water's edge, such as coconut palms of tropical island beaches, produce fruits that can withstand salt water and float on the currents. Mangrove swamp trees form fruits that do not rot when submerged in water.

Bananas are a favorite food of spider monkeys

A young coconut palm sprouting on a beach

HERBACEOUS PLANTS (Bulbs, corms)

Major types:
Bulbs are fat, rounded organs with fleshy food-filled leaves, as in daffodils and snowdrops. **Corms** are rounded, squat, swollen stems produced by crocuses, for example. **Tubers** are fat, oval underground stems with tiny leaves and buds, as in potatoes. **Rhizomes** are long, swollen stems with a bud at one end, as in many grasses and irises.

Bulbs and corms – and the related rhizomes and tubers – are underground food-storage organs of soft-stemmed, or herbaceous, plants that grow from year to year. Such long-lived plants are known as perennials. Trees and shrubs are woody perennials and even in the coldest regions their trunks and branches persist all year round. By contrast, in winter herbaceous perennials either keep some leaves and slow down their growth, as with grasses, or lose all their leaves and remain as a dormant underground form, as with onions and tulips. In both cases, the part that remains underground acts as storage for food which is used for new growth the next spring.

Annual cycle

Plants that produce bulbs, corms and tubers reproduce in two ways, asexually and sexually. The asexual method is often known as vegetative propagation. It involves shoots formed from side buds that develop into roots and leaves, and eventually separate from the parent plant. No flowers, pollination or fertilization of ovules are involved. In daffodils, for example, in the spring an overwintering bulb produces leaves and a flower stalk. While the flower blossoms and its seeds set, the leaves send food down to a de-

veloping side bud which by the end of the growing season has formed a daughter bulb. Vegetative propagation produces clumps of plants which, because of their underground food storage and buds, are resistant to damage and disease.

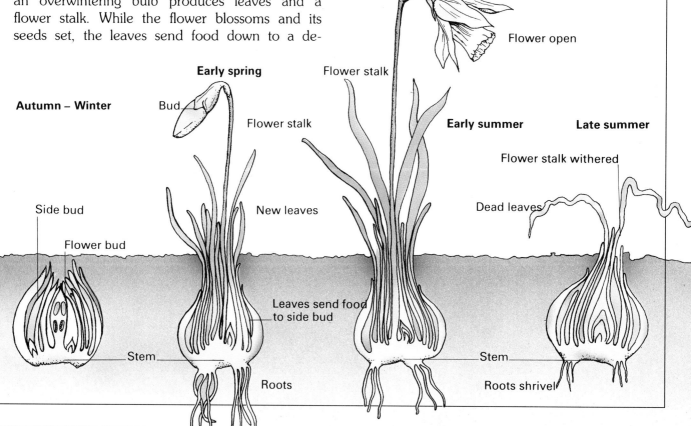

Flower open

Flower stalk

Early spring

Bud

Flower stalk

Autumn – Winter

Early summer　**Late summer**

Flower stalk withered

Side bud

New leaves

Dead leaves

Flower bud

Leaves send food to side bud

Stem

Stem

Roots

Roots shrivel

Flowers

Herbaceous (leafy) perennials include members of the lily and iris families. Common lilies are tulips, hyacinths, onions, garlic and true lilies. Hyacinths are noted for their densely packed heads of scented flowers, and the tiger lily of China for its many varieties with large showy flowers much liked by gardeners. Waterlilies, which are unrelated, produce a thick rhizome form that gives rise to long stalks bearing leaves or flowers that usually lie flat on the surface of the water. The iris family is notable for spectacular flowers. In many species the flowers have equal numbers of upright and drooping petals. Irises include the common crocus and freesias.

Tulips are typical early spring flowers.

Waterlily flowers stick up out of the water.

Life history

Strawberries are perennial clump-forming plants that reproduce asexually – not by forming underground storage organs, but by developing trailing stems, or runners. A new strawberry plant, in its first year, produces a cluster of leaves, flowers, fruits and runners. The following year some of the seeds may germinate and the runners will put down roots and eventually produce new plants. This continues year after year. The strawberries people eat are in fact swollen red fruit stalks; the true fruits are the tiny pips embedded in the surface.

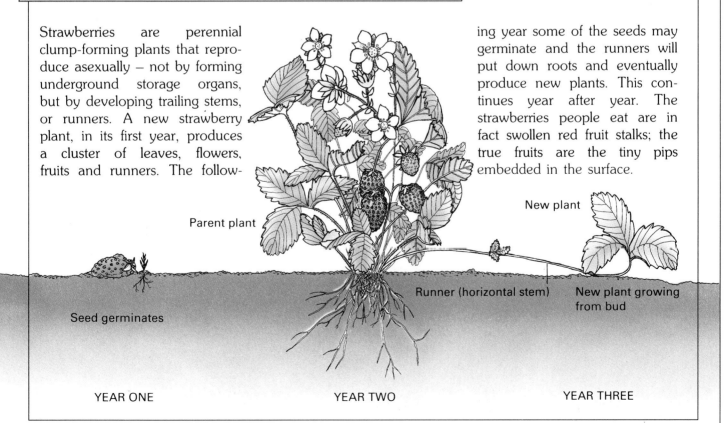

Parent plant

Seed germinates

Runner (horizontal stem)

New plant

New plant growing from bud

YEAR ONE

YEAR TWO

YEAR THREE

Most species are dicotyledons (having two seed leaves). They include the cabbage family such as mustard, radish, turnip, cauliflower and broccoli, and the goosefoot family, for example, spinach and beet. Pansies, marigolds and petunias are typical garden flower species.

In autumn, the aerial parts of herbaceous plants – the stems, leaves and flower stalks – generally die down. Annual species have only one growing season, at the end of which the whole plant dies. Biennials complete their life cycles in two growing seasons. Herbaceous plants also include perennials such as irises. All three types are successful plants because they can grow from seed to flower in sometimes only a few weeks, spreading more rapidly than trees and shrubs that may grow for many years before flowering. However, gardeners in temperate climates regard species such as marigolds as half-hardy, because their seeds cannot withstand frost when germinating.

Shape and form

Meadow species such as poppies grow to 1 m (39 inches) tall, producing branched stalks with deeply divided leaves and roundish showy flowers. Foxgloves grow to 1.5 m (5 feet). They have a single stem topped with a cluster of up to 80 flowers. Alpine plants are usually compact to combat cold windy conditions. Thin flat hairy leaves absorb the maximum amount of light and warmth.

A carpet of alpine plants

Surviving

A sudden frost or snowfall can kill the soft tissues of plants. Species such as the edelweiss have a waxy covering on the leaves that traps heat. The mountain crowfoot has a cell sap containing chemicals that act as an antifreeze. The winter leaf and flower buds of most temperate species are protected by thick, waxy scale leaves, to guard against cold.

Long-stemmed meadow flowers

Frost on nettle leaves

Life history

Annual plants, such as larkspur, fat hen, poppy and chickweed, flower and die in one year. Towards the end of their growing season the flowers make seeds. The seeds are dispersed and remain dormant until the following spring. Then they germinate and the new plants produce leaves and flowers to carry on the species. Biennial plants live for two years. They include wild carrot, cow parsley and cornflower. In the first year they produce only stems and leaves. In the second year they produce more leaves as well as flowers and seeds before dying. Species such as white campion grow as annuals or perennials.

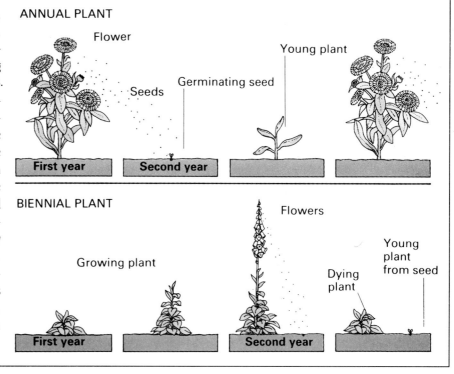

ANNUAL PLANT

Flower

Young plant

Seeds

Germinating seed

First year **Second year**

BIENNIAL PLANT

Flowers

Growing plant

Young plant from seed

Dying plant

First year **Second year**

Seed dispersal

The fruits or seeds of many plants are adapted to travel far from the parent plant to avoid overcrowding. The seeds of dandelions, thistles and clematis have feathery hairs that are caught by the wind. The parachute-like structures fall very slowly to the ground. The pods of peas, beans and lupins dry in the sun, shrivel then burst open to flick out the seeds. Fruits such as tomatoes, strawberries and blackberries are brightly colored and succulent to attract animals. Their fleshy tissues are swallowed and eaten, but the seeds inside the animal are not digested and pass out with the feces. Burdocks produce hooked fruits that catch in the fur of passing animals.

Dandelion
Relies on the wind
for seed dispersal

Pea
Plants of the pea
family produce pods that
throw the seeds out

Tomato
Animals eat the fruit and
disperse the seeds.

Burdock
Hook-like seeds attach
themselves
to animals for dipsersal

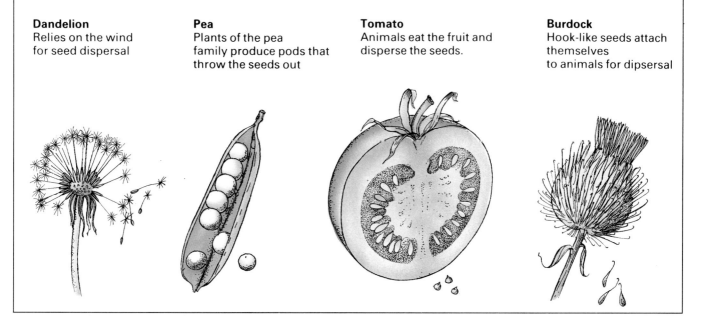

HERBACEOUS PLANTS (Tropical)

Major types:

Cacti are native to dry tropical North and South America and also include the prickly pear plants (opuntias). **Bromeliads** are native to South America. They have leaves that change color. **Orchids** include many species that live on trees. **Succulents** include the desert agaves and euphorbias, which grow to 30 m (100 feet).

In dry scrubland and in deserts, plants have to cope with a constant lack of water. Among adaptations to this, cacti, for example, have no leaves and photosynthesize in their green stems and branches. The lack of leaves prevents them losing the water formed in cell food production. Succulents are plants with thick water-retaining leaves and, like cacti, most have long roots, allowing them to reach water deep underground. In tropical rainforests, orchids and bromeliads grow on the branches of trees where they receive nutrients from rotting vegetation on the bark. The flowers are insect-pollinated and their seeds are usually dispersed by birds and other animals.

Surviving

Cactus is the Greek word for prickly plant, and many cacti bear spiny stems and fruits that deter animals from eating them. Bromeliads in the rain-forest canopy produce roots that are used mainly for attaching the plant to its support. They obtain nutrients from the vase-like container of water and dissolved minerals formed by the circular clump, or rosette, of leaves. Some desert plants stop growing altogether when water supplies dry up. Their seeds germinate only when enough rain falls for them to produce leaves, flowers and fruits before the ground dries again. Similar adaptations in plants of dry grasslands, such as the African savannah, transform a barren land-scape into a sea of flowers as soon as rains start.

Saguaro cactus in the Arizona Desert

A bromeliad clings to another plant for support.

Gourd seed pods wait for rain in the Sahara.

Feeding

The most remarkable feeding habits of plants are found among the pitcher plants. They have enlarged leaves fused together to form a trap for flies, ants and beetles. The jungles of Southeast Asia and Australasia have plants with a cup-shaped pitcher up to 30 cm (12 inches) deep and containing 2 liters (3.4 pints) of water. Insects are attracted to the pitcher by smell, color and a sugary fluid around the rim. As they enter they lose their footing, fall into the water and drown. Glands at the base of the pitcher produce chemicals that digest the animal food to provide essential minerals for the plant.

An Asian pitcher plant traps insects for food.

Flowers

The largest flower in the world is that of the rafflesia plant of Malaysia. The plant, which has no proper stem or leaves, grows on the branches of a vine tree absorbing water and nutrients from the host. The flower grows to 1 m (39 inches) across but lasts only a week. Orchids produce flowers with a lip that has a distinctive color or shape to attract insects or even small birds for pollination. In bee orchids, the lip resembles a female bee and males visit the flowers expecting to mate. The banana family includes the bird of paradise and ginger plants. Several South American plants have flowers pollinated by hummingbirds which, with their thin beaks and long tongues, are the only animals able to reach the nectar at the base.

The agave is pollinated by hummingbirds.

GRASSES

There are nearly 10,000 species of grasses and the related reeds and rushes. They form one of the largest families of flowering plants and are the most important economically. Either as cereals or as forage for farm animals, they are the main source of food for most people in the world. All are monocotyledons (having a single seed-leaf) with ribbon-like leaves, upright stems and thread-like roots. The flowers are tiny and are often clustered together in units called spikelets. They can rapidly colonize waste land. Among cereals, wheat is the major species of temperate regions, rice of tropical Asia and Africa, and maize, or corn, of tropical South America.

Structure and form

The stems of grasses are usually circular and hollow, and they bear long narrow leaves. The lower part of each leaf is wrapped around the stem. Underground, buds develop into new side-shoots to form a clump of stems, and many species spread like weeds by producing rhizomes or runners each with several growing points. Flowers develop at the top of stems in groups known as spikelets. They are adapted for wind pollination. They usually lack petals and sepals and have feathery stigmas and large anthers that hang outside the protective bracts so that wind shakes the pollen free.

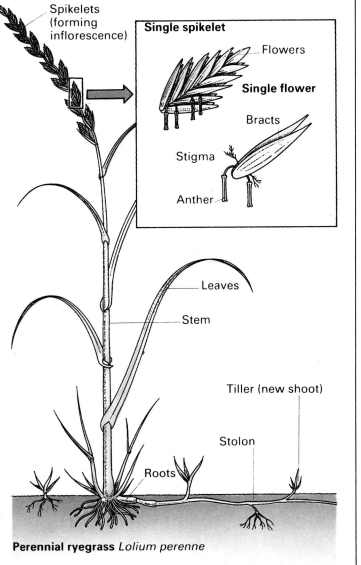

Perennial ryegrass *Lolium perenne*

Tufts of bunch grass in the Andes Mountains

Seeds

The seeds of cereal grasses can be quite large, as in maize (corn), and contain large amounts of nutritious carbohydrates, or sugars. Rice and maize, for example, are the staple diets of many countries. Barley grains are a source of malt used for brewing, and wheat provides flour for making bread and pasta. The flower head is often called an ear and the individual seeds, grains. Winnowing is the removal of the grains from the rest of the ear, the chaff, by wind or air currents. Modern cereals are the result of thousands of years of selection and breeding to produce crops that will grow in almost any given climate and which will be resistant to pests.

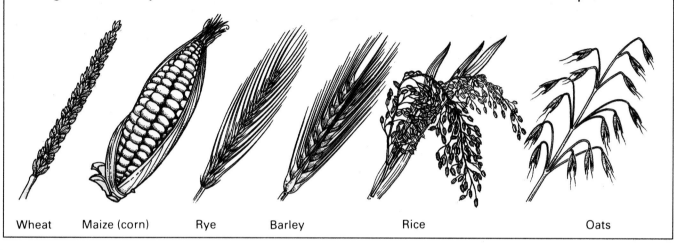

Wheat   Maize (corn)   Rye   Barley   Rice   Oats

Habitats

Grasses are extremely common and widely distributed, and grow in temperate chalkland areas, in tropical swamps and rainforests, in desert and on high mountains. The grasslands of the world include the steppes of central Asia, the prairies of North America and the savannahs of Africa. Bamboos grow mostly in tropical regions and, as in parts of Southeast Asia, often form dense forests. Their stems grow to 30 m (100 ft) high and 50 cm (20 inches) in diameter. They bear leaves all the way up, but as the bamboo gets older, leaves drop from the lower part of the stem. Reeds grow along ditches, ponds and lakes. Rushes colonize bogs and marshes in all parts of the world except the tropics.

Reeds fringing a lake in southern France

Giant bamboos growing in Sri Lanka

Flowering plants chart

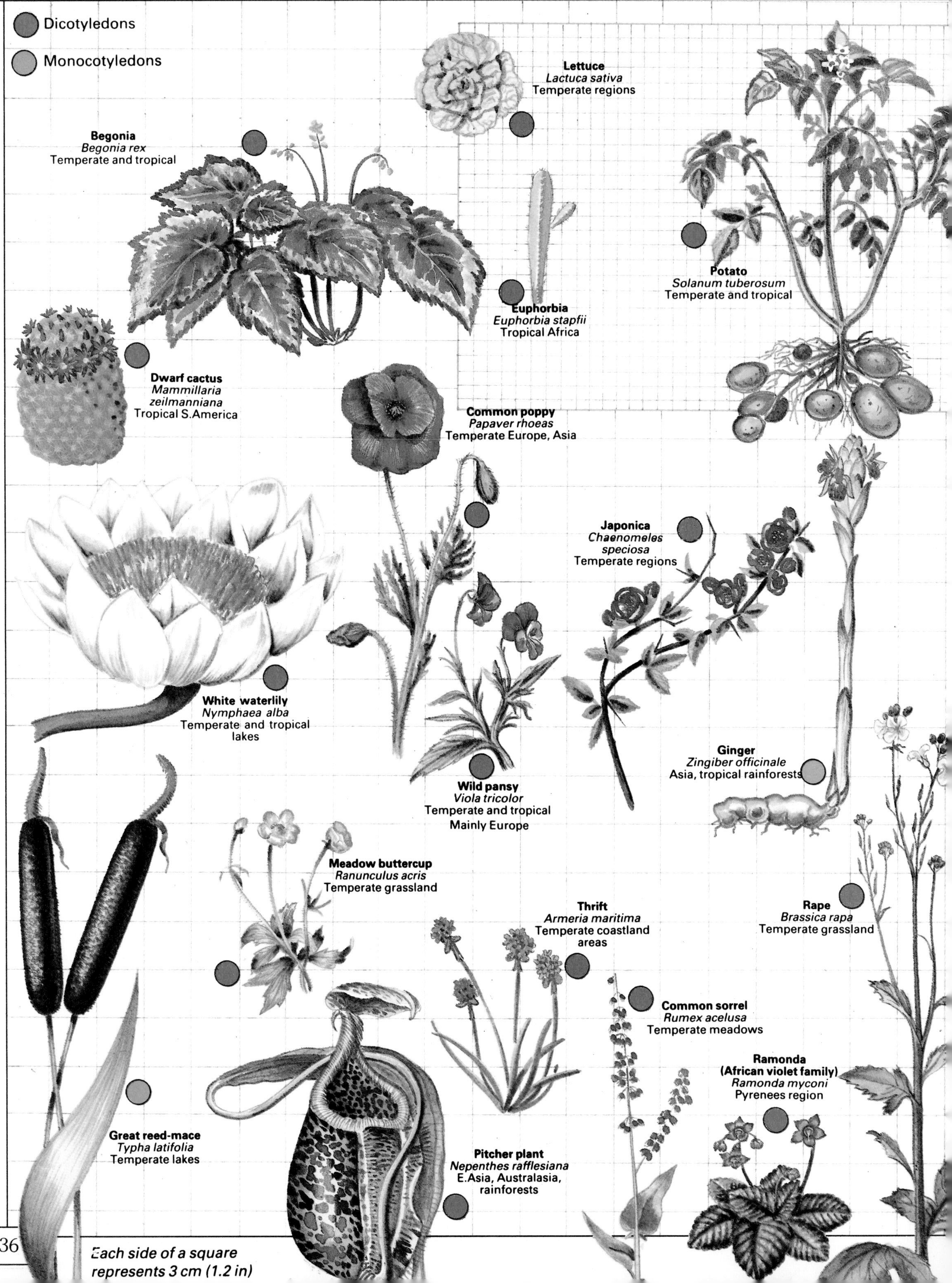

- ● Dicotyledons
- ● Monocotyledons

Lettuce
Lactuca sativa
Temperate regions

Begonia
Begonia rex
Temperate and tropical

Potato
Solanum tuberosum
Temperate and tropical

Euphorbia
Euphorbia stapfii
Tropical Africa

Dwarf cactus
*Mammillaria
zeilmanniana*
Tropical S.America

Common poppy
Papaver rhoeas
Temperate Europe, Asia

Japonica
*Chaenomeles
speciosa*
Temperate regions

White waterlily
Nymphaea alba
Temperate and tropical
lakes

Ginger
Zingiber officinale
Asia, tropical rainforests

Wild pansy
Viola tricolor
Temperate and tropical
Mainly Europe

Meadow buttercup
Ranunculus acris
Temperate grassland

Thrift
Armeria maritima
Temperate coastland
areas

Rape
Brassica rapa
Temperate grassland

Common sorrel
Rumex acelusa
Temperate meadows

**Ramonda
(African violet family)**
Ramonda myconi
Pyrenees region

Great reed-mace
Typha latifolia
Temperate lakes

Pitcher plant
Nepenthes rafflesiana
E.Asia, Australasia,
rainforests

36

*Each side of a square
represents 3 cm (1.2 in)*

Fig
Ficus carica
Native of W.Asia

Magnolia
Magnolia x soulangeana
Native of E.Asia

Cactus
Carnegiea gigantea
S.America deserts

London Plane
Platanus x hispanica
Temperate regions

Lemon
Citrus limon
Mediterranean, but
grown worldwide

Pineapple
Ananas comosus
Native of tropical
S.America

Chusan palm
Trachycarpus excelsus
Tropical Asia

Olive
Olea europaea
Mediterranean region

Silver birch
Betula pendula
Temperate Europe and
Asia

Mistletoe
Viscum album
Tropical and temperate
regions

Bay laurel
Laurus nobilis
Native of Mediterranean
region

Peony
Paeonia peregrina
Temperate regions

Cider gum
Eucalyptus gunnii
Australia, dry areas

Weeping willow
Salix babylonica
Native of China and Far
East

Common nettle
Urtica dioica
Tropical and temperate
meadow

Baobab
Adansonia digitalis
Central and S.Africa

Horse chestnut
Aesculus hippocastanum
N. Hemisphere,
temperate

Common oak
Quercus robur
Temperate regions

Each side of a square represents 10 m (33ft)

37

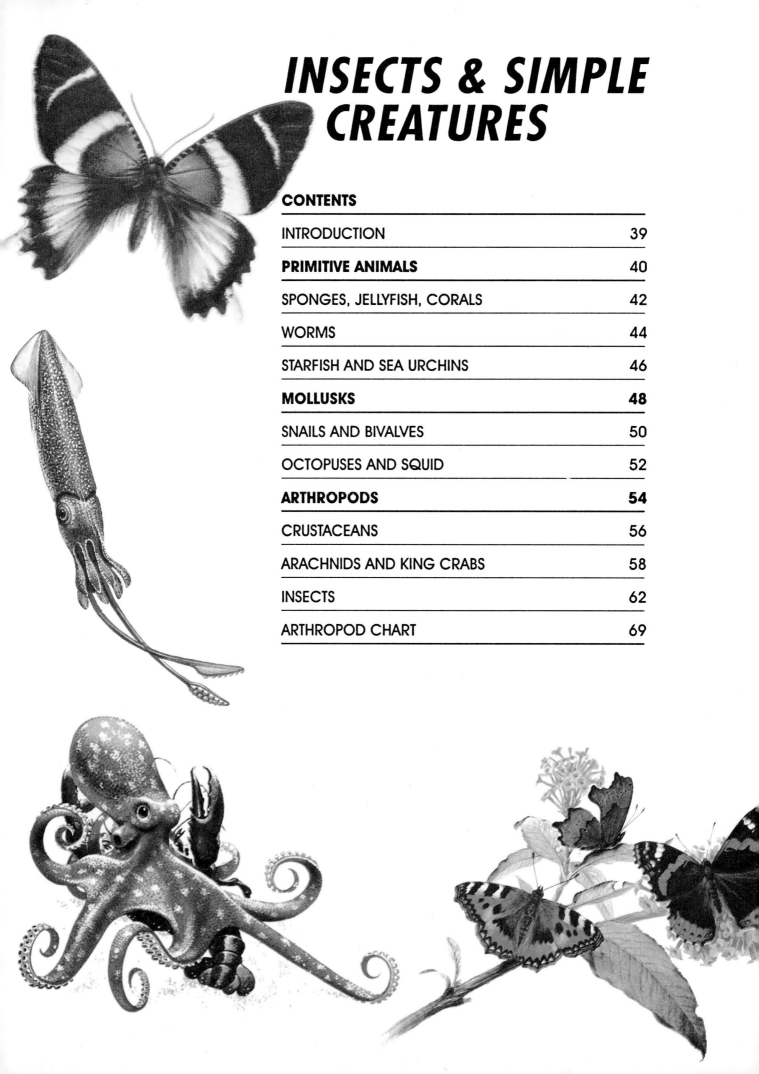

INSECTS & SIMPLE CREATURES

CONTENTS

INTRODUCTION

Simple creatures – animals lacking a backbone – make up the vast majority of species on Earth. They have existed since its First Life forms evolved, conquering every habitat – water, land and air. For example, there is no place on Earth that does not have some form of insect life.

Life first evolved in water and today the world's oceans and rivers team with simple creatures. These range from microscopic single-celled creatures, that float in surface waters such as plankton, to larger colonial animals such as corals and jellyfish. In the sea some soft-bodied animals developed a hard protective covering, such as shellfish. Others developed limbs and gave rise to today's crustaceans such as lobsters and shrimps. On the land and in the air jointed-legged animals – arthropods – gave rise to insects and spiders. Only insects have developed the power of flight, and they remain the predominant life form on Earth.

Scientists call animals with no backbone invertebrates. Although almost all birds and mammals have been discovered, most scientists think that there may still be at least 8 million different kinds of invertebrates still to be found.

PRIMITIVE ANIMALS

Single-celled animals are known as Protozoa. There are more than 30,000 species.
Major types:
Flagellates such as the pond animal called euglena.
Sarcodines, for instance amoeba, which moves and feeds using "false feet" (pseudopodia). **Ciliates**, such as the pond species paramecium, which is covered in tiny hairs called cilia. **Spore-forming** types, most of which are parasites, such as plasmodium.

All living things, from a tiny flea to a whale, are made up of microscopic cells. Cells are the building blocks of life, the smallest units of life that can exist on their own. Most living things are made up of many cells – they are multicellular. In such animals and plants, there are several different types of cells, each adapted for different jobs, for example nerve and muscle cells. Multicellular life-forms can each be thought of as an assembled machine. Their cells are grouped together to make various tissues, tissues combine to make organs, and all the organs combine to make up the complete animal. There are, however, many unicellular life-forms – animals and plants consisting of just one cell. These represent the simplest forms of life and were the first living things to evolve on Earth some 3,000 million years ago.

Animal cells

A typical single-celled animal is spherical or oval in shape and measures about 0.03mm (0.001in) across. In simple multicellular animals such as jellyfish, the cells are arranged as two layers – the inner endoderm and outer ectoderm. In between the layers is the jelly-like mesogloea. In higher multicellular animals there are three layers and the mesogloea is replaced by the central cell layer called the mesoderm.

Nucleus
Controlling the overall activity of the cell is the central nucleus. It contains the chromosomes, which are long strands of special chemicals that form a genetic blueprint of living things.

Cell membrane
The membrane is a soft, pliable skin which contains the cytoplasm and controls the flow of nutrients and waste products into and out of the cell.

Endoplasmic reticulum
This is a network of flattened sacs and tubes that form a communications link between the nucleus and the cell's surroundings.

Cytoplasm
Most of the cell consists of a watery fluid, the cytoplasm, in which all the structures are embedded.

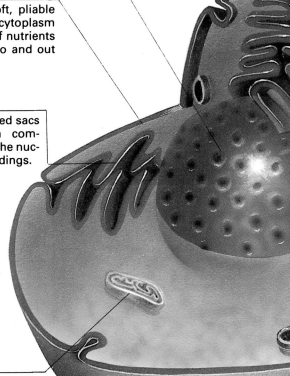

Two-layered

Ectoderm
Endoderm
Mesogloea
Body cavity

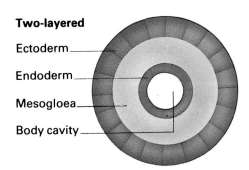

Three-layered

Ectoderm
Endoderm
Mesoderm
Gut

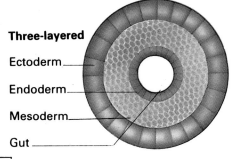

Mitochondrion
Energy needed for all the cell's activity is produced in the many oval-shaped mitochondria. They are the cell's powerhouses.

Feeding

Among single-celled animals, one group – the sarcodines – have a simple feeding action. This can be seen in the common pond animal, amoeba. When a piece of food comes in contact with the cell membrane, an amoeba pushes out a 'foot' that surrounds the food. With a pincer-like action, it engulfs the food and forms a vacuole or sac in the cytoplasm. Filling this with special chemicals, it digests the food.

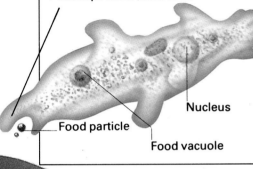

Pseudopodium (false foot)

Food particle

Nucleus

Food vacuole

TYPICAL ANIMAL CELL
× 5,000

Life cycle

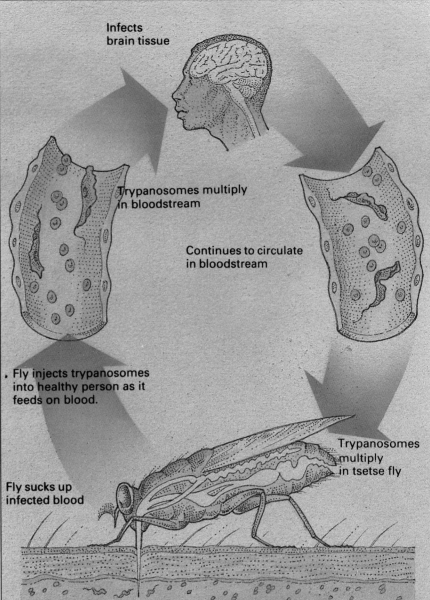

Infects brain tissue

Trypanosomes multiply in bloodstream

Continues to circulate in bloodstream

Fly injects trypanosomes into healthy person as it feeds on blood.

Trypanosomes multiply in tsetse fly

Fly sucks up infected blood

Single-celled protozoa, although simple in structure, have evolved a wide variety of lifestyles and are adapted to great extremes of availability of food. Many of them are parasites, depending on another animal, the host, for food. Some of these, such as the trypanosome parasite, cause diseases in humans. A species of trypanosome found in Africa has a life cycle involving two hosts, the tsetse fly and a human. It causes the human disease called sleeping sickness. The life cycle starts when the tsetse fly, the first host, feeds by chance on an infected person's blood. With its long pointed proboscis, or feeding tube, the fly pierces the skin to reach a blood vessel. It sucks up trypanosomes along with the blood. When the fly then feeds on a healthy person, the trypanosomes are transferred to a new human host. There they are carried around in the bloodstream to the brain, where they cause serious damage.

SPONGES, JELLYFISH, CORALS

Major types:
Sponges (over 5,000 species) include those animals with supporting spikes of chalk or silica, such as in glass sponges, or of soft spongin, as in bath sponges.
Jellyfish (200), sea anemones and corals (6,500) and hydroids (2,700), such as hydra.

Sponges are the simplest of multicellular animals. Each is just a two-layered bag of cells, with each cell working alone, engulfing and digesting food particles. Some of the cells form spikes that together give the animal support and shape. Jellyfish, corals and the related sea anemones also have a two-layered structure but groups of similar cells are arranged to form tissues, and groups of tissues make organs, structures that have a definite function. The two cell layers surround the hollow body cavity which is open at one end to form a mouth. Around the mouth are tentacles that carry poisonous stings. Jellyfish and their relatives all feed on other water animals.

Life cycle

Sponges, most corals, and sea anemones spend their life attached to rocks. They are often found in huge masses, as on tropical ocean reefs. Jellyfish are free to float in the water and are carried round oceans by the currents. Hydroids such as *Obelia* are small animals related to jellyfish that have a very complex life cycle with two totally different structural types: a slender, cylindrical, plant-like form, the polyp, which stays fixed to seaweed or rocks, and an umbrella-shaped free-swimming form, the medusa. The polyp grows and produces offshoots so that a colony of individuals forms. It also forms outgrowths which develop into medusae. As the medusae become fully formed, they break off the parent animal and float away. Each tiny medusa then produces sperm or eggs. The eggs are fertilized in the water and develop into hairy larvae, called planulae. These find a suitable resting place, and develop into new polyps.

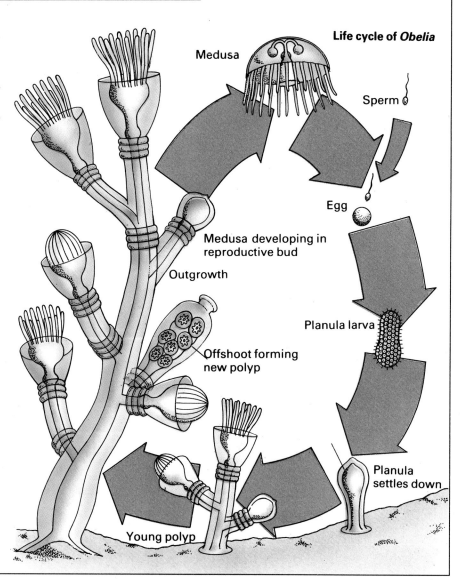

Life cycle of *Obelia*

Medusa

Sperm

Egg

Medusa developing in reproductive bud

Outgrowth

Planula larva

Offshoot forming new polyp

Planula settles down

Young polyp

Feeding

Sponges have special cells called collar cells which bear a long whip-like hair, a flagellum. By beating the flagella, the cells draw water and food particles into the body cavity. The tentacles of jellyfish, sea anemones and hydroids bear cells which paralyse live prey. The tentacles are used to pull food to the mouth. Many of these animals have tiny plants – algae – living inside their bodies, and both benefit from the arrangement. Corals and anemones digest animal food and use the products for energy. Carbon dioxide is formed as a waste. The algae are plants and make use of photosynthesis, using sunlight as energy to combine carbon dioxide and water to form sugars. Oxygen is produced as a waste. Corals supply the algae with carbon dioxide, and the algae produce oxygen for the corals.

Sea anemones use tentacles to catch food.

Offense and defense

Jellyfish, such as the sea nettle and the Portuguese man-o'war, live in the sea and have trailing tentacles, some carrying stings. The largest type of jellyfish is 2.3 m (7.5 feet) across with tentacles 30 m (98 feet) long. The sting is produced by special cells and is used to stun and capture prey ranging in size from plankton to fish up to 30cm (12in) long. All the relatives of anemones are equipped with deadly weapons in the form of cells that act like spring-guns. Each cell consists of a tightly coiled thread would into a capsule, with a trigger hair on the outside. When the prey swims against the trigger, the thread is shot out and snares the unsuspecting animal.

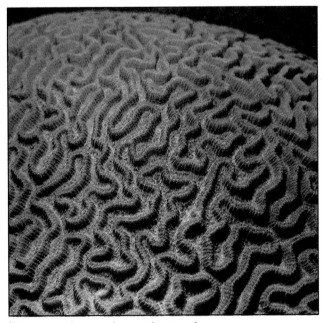
Brain coral is a colony of animals.

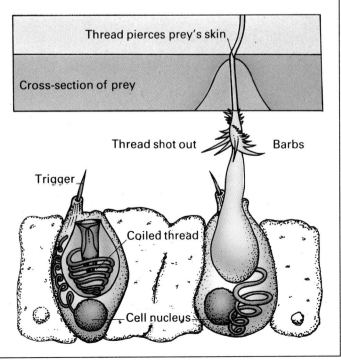
Thread pierces prey's skin

Cross-section of prey

Thread shot out — Barbs

Trigger

Coiled thread

Cell nucleus

WORMS

Major types:

Flatworms – simple body plan, unsegmented – e.g. tapeworms (1,500 species), flukes (2,400).

Ribbon worms – unsegmented, covered in tiny hairs (750).

Roundworms – unsegmented, covered in a protective cuticle (over 10,000).

Segmented worms, the annelids, bristleworms (4,000), earthworms (2,500) and leeches (300).

The name worm is commonly used for any long, thin, tubular invertebrate animal, but scientists distinguish many different types. The familiar earthworm and bloodsucking leech are segmented worms. Tapeworms, which people sometimes can get from eating undercooked meat containing their larvae, are parasitic flatworms, while the carnivorous *Planaria* (shown below) of ponds are free-living species. A parasite of sheep, the liver fluke, has a flattened body and does not look like a worm but is related to *Planaria*. Earthworms, instead of a cavity type gut, have a digestive tube with a front and back opening. Roundworms have an unsegmented body covered with a thick horny layer (cuticle).

Structure

The common feature of worms is a three-layered body plan. The middle layer of cells, the mesoderm, often has separate structures such as muscles and blood vessels. Flatworms such as *Planaria* show many of the characteristic features of worms. There is a distinct head region bearing the beginnings of a brain and sense organs such as eyes. The digestive system runs the length of the body and is branched to ensure that all parts receive digested food. Nerve cords extend from the head down each side of the body and allow coordinated actions. If the worm is cut in half, the head end grows a new "tail."

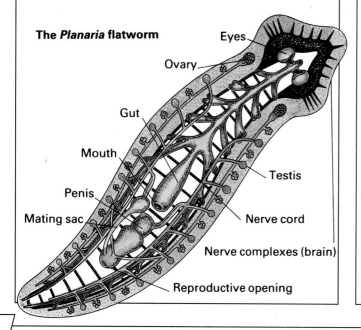

The *Planaria* flatworm

Eyes

Ovary

Gut

Mouth

Penis

Mating sac

Testis

Nerve cord

Nerve complexes (brain)

Reproductive opening

Mating

A host animal can rarely support two adult parasitic worms, making normal mating difficult. Such worms are hermaphrodites – adapted so that an individual's male cells, sperm, can fertilize its own female sex cells, the eggs. Most free-living worms such as earthworms are also hermaphrodite but the eggs of one worm must be fertilized by the sperm from another. At mating time two earthworms lie together head to tail and form slimy envelopes around their reproductive segments, exchanging eggs and sperm. The worms then separate and later each produces and deposits a series of sacs of fertilized eggs.

Earthworms lie together to mate.

Life cycle

Worms such as the tapeworm and liver fluke have a life cycle involving two different hosts and many developmental stages. The fluke, for example, lives as an adult in sheep. The worm produces fertilized eggs that pass out of this first host along with undigested food. Each egg develops into an immature form, a larva, that to survive must be eaten by the second host, a snail. In the snail, the larva multiplies and passes through other larval stages. Individuals of one such stage escape from the snail and form a protective coat around themselves. Only when eaten by a sheep will they change into the adult form. Although the worm's parasitic lifestyle requires being eaten by the right animal at the right time, its food is provided by the hosts.

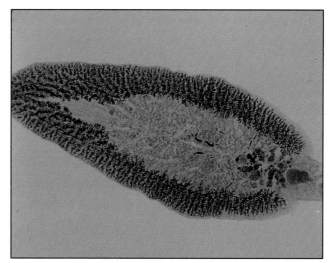
The liver fluke is a parasite of sheep and snails.

Feeding

Garden worms such as earthworms, and worms that live on sandy or muddy beaches, such as lugworms, swallow soil or sand and feed by digesting particles of animal and plant food contained in this. Most free-living flatworms engulf their food by enclosing it in the mouth-like opening to their gut. Feather worms, which burrow in the seabed, bear feathery gills that also act as food-collectors, directing plankton toward the mouth. Parasites in general have no need for an elaborate digestive system because all their food is pre-processed by the host. Some tapeworms have no real gut at all. They simply absorb nutrients through their body wall. The worm's cuticle protects it from the host's digestive juices, and it avoids being washed along the host's digestive system by means of suckers and hooks on its front portion.

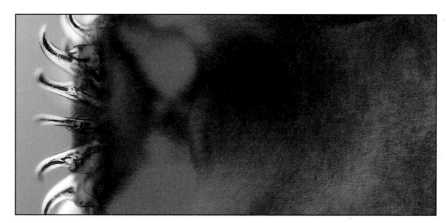
A tapeworm holds on using hooks on its head.

Lugworms leave casts near their burrows in the mud.

STARFISH AND SEA URCHINS

Starfish, sea urchins and their relatives are marine animals that form a group called echinoderms, which means spiny skinned. Beneath their outer surface is a rigid skeleton made up of plates of the chemical calcium carbonate (chalk). Often these plates bear spines that can be painful for an unwary swimmer. Echinoderms have no head, no true brain, and are unsegmented. The mouth is usually on the underside of the body. Unlike most animals, their body is built on a five-fold plan so that instead of only two sections of the body that are identical to one another, there are five. This body plan and lack of a brain limits their movements. All live in shallow or deep seas worldwide.

Major types:
Starfish (1,600 species) have between 5 and 40 arms and move using tube feet.
Brittle stars (2,000) move mostly using their arms not tube feet.
Sea urchins (800) lack arms and are spherical in shape.
Sea cucumbers (900) lack arms and are elongated.
Sea lilies (80) fixed on sea bed, and **Feather-stars** (540).

Structure

Starfish and brittle stars have five or more arms radiating from a central disk. The disk bears a water-filled ring canal and tube feet stick through holes in the skeletal plates. By means of water pressure in the canal system, the feet can be extended or retracted. At the tip of each foot is a sucker. Tube feet are used to collect food and for movement. Sea urchins and other echinoderms have similar tube feet or lack feet completely, instead using their arms for movement.

A five-armed brittle star

Feeding

Most starfish are meat-eaters. They prey upon shellfish such as scallops, prying open the shell with their tube feet. Brittle stars and most sea lilies and sea cucumbers feed on plankton and morsels of decaying matter. By beating the tiny hairs, cilia, covering their tube feet, they funnel the food to their mouth. Sea urchins have a diet consisting of both animal and plant food. Sea cucumbers living at great depths swallow sediment from the seabed and extract food from it.

A sea urchin's central mouth

A European starfish feeding on a bed of mussels

Life cycle

Echinoderms have amazing powers of regeneration – that is, if they lose part of the body a new part grows within a few days or weeks. Some starfish reproduce in this way, pulling themselves apart into several portions, each of which then grows into a complete animal. Generally, though, echinoderms reproduce sexually, with males releasing millions of sperm into the water and females releasing eggs. The fertilized eggs develop into free-swimming larvae that gradually grow into adults. Among some species, the fertilized eggs are kept within the female's body and the offspring are born as tiny replicas.

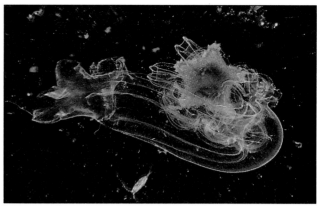

A newly hatched starfish larva

Primitive creatures chart

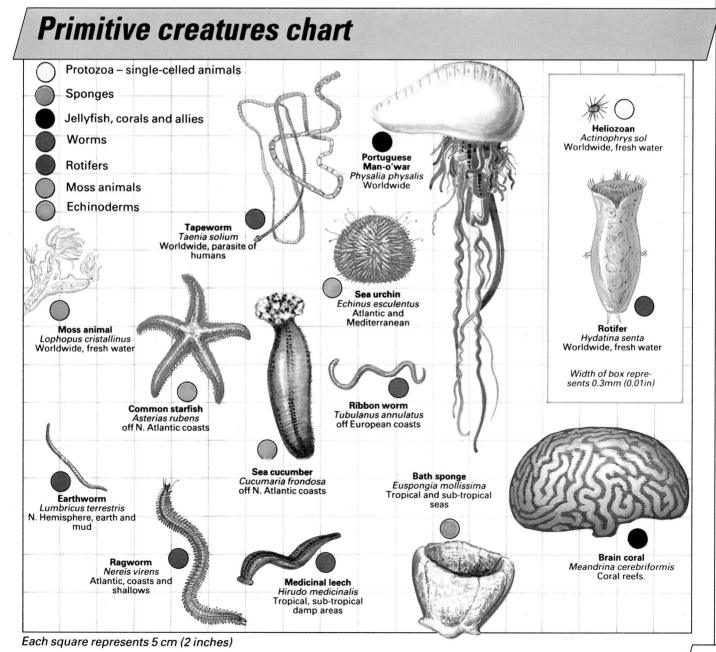

Protozoa – single-celled animals

Sponges

Jellyfish, corals and allies

Worms

Rotifers

Moss animals

Echinoderms

Heliozoan
Actinophrys sol
Worldwide, fresh water

Portuguese Man-o'war
Physalia physalis
Worldwide

Tapeworm
Taenia solium
Worldwide, parasite of humans

Sea urchin
Echinus esculentus
Atlantic and Mediterranean

Rotifer
Hydatina senta
Worldwide, fresh water

Width of box represents 0.3mm (0.01in)

Moss animal
Lophopus cristallinus
Worldwide, fresh water

Common starfish
Asterias rubens
off N. Atlantic coasts

Ribbon worm
Tubulanus annulatus
off European coasts

Sea cucumber
Cucumaria frondosa
off N. Atlantic coasts

Bath sponge
Euspongia mollissima
Tropical and sub-tropical seas

Earthworm
Lumbricus terrestris
N. Hemisphere, earth and mud

Ragworm
Nereis virens
Atlantic, coasts and shallows

Medicinal leech
Hirudo medicinalis
Tropical, sub-tropical damp areas

Brain coral
Meandrina cerebriformis
Coral reefs.

Each square represents 5 cm (2 inches)

MOLLUSKS

Major types:
Chitons (1,150 species) are flat and oval, with a broad flat foot.
Snails and limpets (40,000) have a large shell; their allies, the slugs, have none.
Bivalves (8,000), such as cockles and mussels, have a mantle divided into two, each forming half of a hinged shell.
Squid, cuttlefish and octopuses (750) lack an external shell.

Most primitive invertebrates are small animals that live in the sea. An increase in size and ability to live on land require special adaptations such as a brain for complex coordinated actions, lungs for breathing, and an extensive blood system for carrying nutrients to all parts of the body. Protection for soft internal organs is also important. Mollusks are a varied group of some 50,000 invertebrates, with each species showing one or more of these adaptations. Although bivalves lack a head, mollusks' bodies are unsegmented and generally divided into a head, a muscular foot and a humped back covered by a large fold of skin, the mantle. In most mollusks the mantle produces a protective shell.

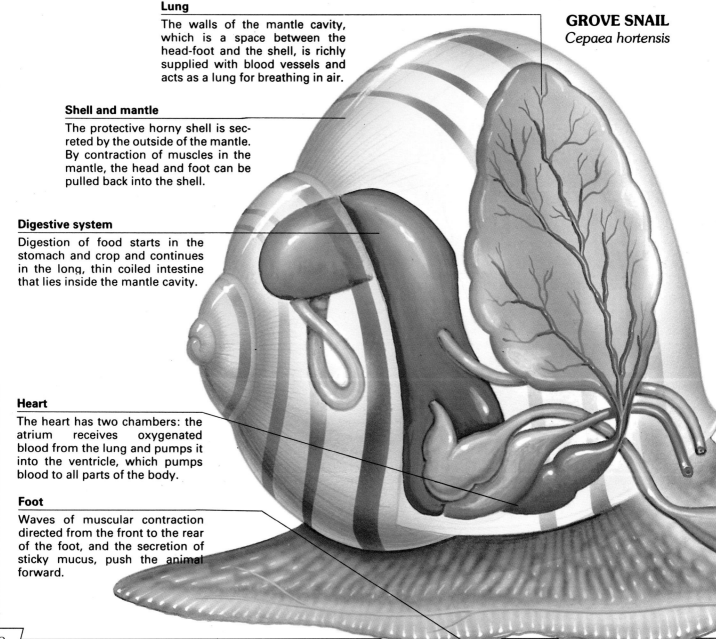

GROVE SNAIL
Cepaea hortensis

Lung
The walls of the mantle cavity, which is a space between the head-foot and the shell, is richly supplied with blood vessels and acts as a lung for breathing in air.

Shell and mantle
The protective horny shell is secreted by the outside of the mantle. By contraction of muscles in the mantle, the head and foot can be pulled back into the shell.

Digestive system
Digestion of food starts in the stomach and crop and continues in the long, thin coiled intestine that lies inside the mantle cavity.

Heart
The heart has two chambers: the atrium receives oxygenated blood from the lung and pumps it into the ventricle, which pumps blood to all parts of the body.

Foot
Waves of muscular contraction directed from the front to the rear of the foot, and the secretion of sticky mucus, push the animal forward.

The shell

Chitons have a shell consisting of eight plates. In snails and limpets the shell is usually cone-shaped and whorled. Clams, mussels and other bivalves have a shell in two halves. In cuttlefish and octopus the shell is internal or absent altogether.

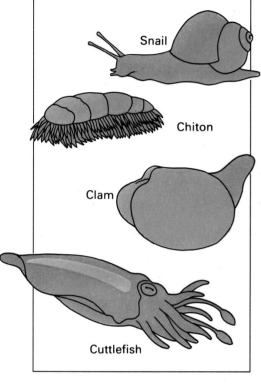

Snail

Chiton

Clam

Cuttlefish

Life cycle

Mollusks such as oysters have a life cycle with several larval stages. Reproduction involves adults shedding many sperm and eggs into the water. Fertilized eggs not eaten by other animals develop into free-swimming larvae that have a tiny shell and a fringe of hairs (cilia) for moving about and feeding. At the next larval stages the shell enlarges, the foot develops and the internal organs become fully formed. The last larva, the spat, eventually attaches itself to a rock and grows into an adult oyster.

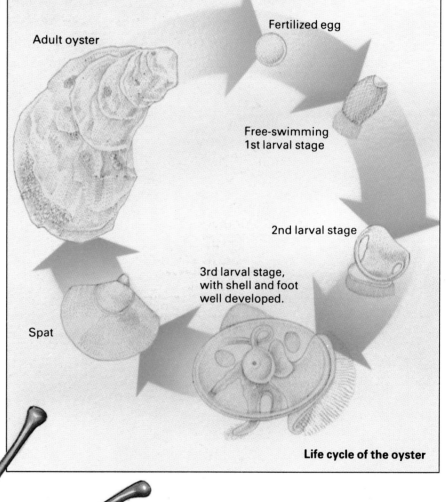

Adult oyster

Fertilized egg

Free-swimming
1st larval stage

2nd larval stage

3rd larval stage,
with shell and foot
well developed.

Spat

Life cycle of the oyster

Nervous system

The head bears two large nerve-tissue swellings that together act like a brain and from which nerves run the length of the head-foot.

Mouth

A feature of slugs and snails is a mouth bearing a radula, a rasping tongue, with which the animals eat plants or animals.

SNAILS AND BIVALVES

There are more than 8,000 species of bivalves and 40,000 species of snails and their allies, the limpets, slugs, sea hares and sea butterflies. They are distributed worldwide but mostly in temperate and warm seas and land areas.
Largest: giant clam of Indo-Pacific coral reefs – 135cm (54in) long and 330kg (730lb).
Smallest: coinshell, a bivalve, in the Atlantic – 0.5mm (0.02in)

Snails, slugs and limpets are the most successful of mollusks. There are species fully adapted to life in the sea, such as lovely colored tropical sea slugs. Different kinds of snails are found in gardens, ponds and lakes. Limpets and winkles inhabit seashores worldwide. Bivalves is a term often used for mollusks that have a shell divided into two halves and gills for breathing and for straining food particles from water. They inhabit estuaries and shallow waters. Some bivalves, such as razor shells, are burrowing animals, and others, for instance mussels, spend their lives attached to a firm base such as a rock. Bivalves include among others cockles, mussels, oysters and clams.

Feeding and breathing

Land snails and slugs breathe with lungs and feed by rasping at their food. Aquatic species breathe using gills that lie within the mantle cavity. Sea slugs lack a shell, and the gills are clearly visible as feathery structures on the top of the animal. Bivalves, too, breathe using gills. Water is drawn into the cavity via an inlet siphon or tube. Exchange of oxygen and carbon dioxide takes place between the water and the mollusk's blood. Used water moves out of the cavity through an outlet siphon. Bivalves are filter feeders, sifting food from water drawn in for breathing. The gills are covered with sticky mucus, which traps the food, and with cilia, which moves it towards the mouth. Siphons and gills can be seen between the halves of the shell.

A pond snail breathes using internal gills.

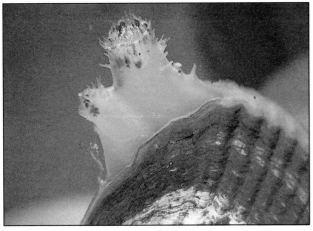

The siphons of a cockle

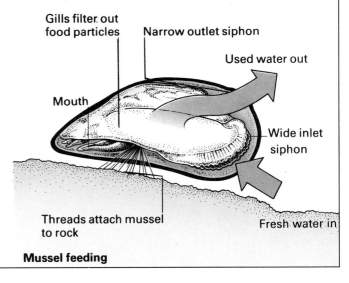

Gills filter out food particles
Narrow outlet siphon
Used water out
Mouth
Wide inlet siphon
Threads attach mussel to rock
Fresh water in

Mussel feeding

Mating

Mollusks such as the edible snail have both male and female sex organs. But mating is essential because an animal cannot fertilize its own eggs. Two snails come together and each shoots a chemical 'love dart' into the other's body. This stimulates the exchange of sperm between the two animals. The eggs are fertilized within the snails' bodies. After mating the snails move apart and each lays several batches of eggs in the soil or under stones. Some snails die after mating. The eggs hatch into tiny snails several weeks later. Among aquatic slugs and snails, most species reproduce like the land snail and release ribbons of fertilized eggs, but some shed their eggs and sperm into the water and fertilization happens there. Larvae hatch from the eggs.

Mating snails exchange sperm.

Movement

Sea hares and sea butterflies move by means of flat extensions of the foot that are used like paddles. Movement in limpets and most slugs and snails is produced by waves of contraction of the muscular foot. Bivalves such as clams and razor shells use their foot to burrow into sand. The foot is pushed into the sand, expanded to provide anchorage, then contracted to pull the animal downwards. This is achieved by forcing blood in and out of the foot and water in and out of the mantle cavity. Piddocks are bivalves that can burrow into rock, using their foot as a lever to move the shell to and fro and rasp against the surface to make a hollow. Scallops can propel themselves forward by opening the gap in the shell, the valve, and closing it quickly to force out a jet of water.

An Australian sea slug swims by body undulations.

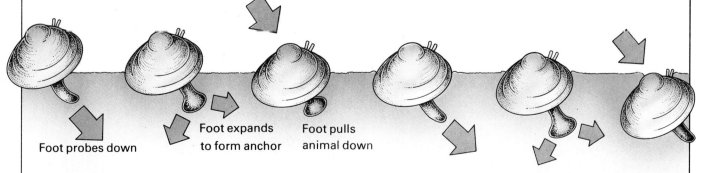

Foot probes down

Foot expands to form anchor

Foot pulls animal down

Clam burrowing into sand

Sequence repeated to burrow deeper

OCTOPUSES AND SQUID

Major types:
Squid and cuttlefish have a small internal shell.
Octopuses lack a shell.
Nautiluses are the only kinds with a complete external shell.
Cephalopods are marine animals of warm and temperate waters and include the largest known invertebrate, the giant deep sea squid, Architeuthis, which can be up to 18m (60ft) long.

The largest and most intelligent of all invertebrates are found among the cephalopods, a group of 700 or so mollusks that includes octopuses, squids and cuttlefish. Cephalopod means head-foot, and these animals have a well-developed head bearing a very efficient nerve complex – like a true brain – and sense organs such as eyes and balancing organs. The head is surrounded by a circle of arms or sucker-bearing tentacles, which are modifications of the mollusk foot used for feeding. The foot is also adapted to form a muscular tube, the siphon, through which water enters and leaves the mantle cavity for gill breathing. This also provides the method of propulsion for cephalopods.

Swimming and hunting

Cephalopods move by jet propulsion, squirting water out of the mantle cavity through the siphon. Most octopuses, however, which spend their lives on the inshore seabed, crawl using their tentacles rather than swim. Cephalopods live as predators, feeding on fish, crustaceans and shellfish. Squid live in the open sea and cuttlefish on the seabed. Squid have eight tentacles, and a further two that are retractible and particularly long and used to seize prey. Octopuses have eight tentacles, which they wrap around their victims, and a poisonous bite. Nautiluses, which inhabit tropical waters, have many arms. Species such as the beautiful pearly nautilus have as many as 100, but they lack suckers.

A cuttlefish has a shell inside its body.

Suckered tentacles of a giant octopus

A nautilus moves by jet propulsion.

Reproduction

Among squid, cuttlefish and nautiluses especially, individuals often perform a courtship display before mating. This is often associated with color changes in the animals. As a male encounters another of his kind, his color deepens. If the visitor fails to similarly change color, it is assumed to be a female and is approached. During mating the male uses one of his arms to deposit packets of sperm into the female's mantle cavity. Here fertilization of the eggs occurs. Most cephalopods lay their eggs in clusters on the seabed, where they are left to develop and grow into small versions of the adults. The young spend their first few months in surface waters.

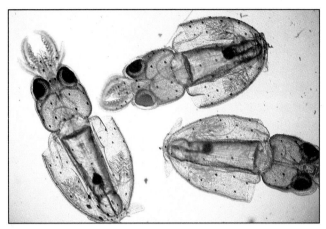

Baby squid just after hatching

Mollusk chart

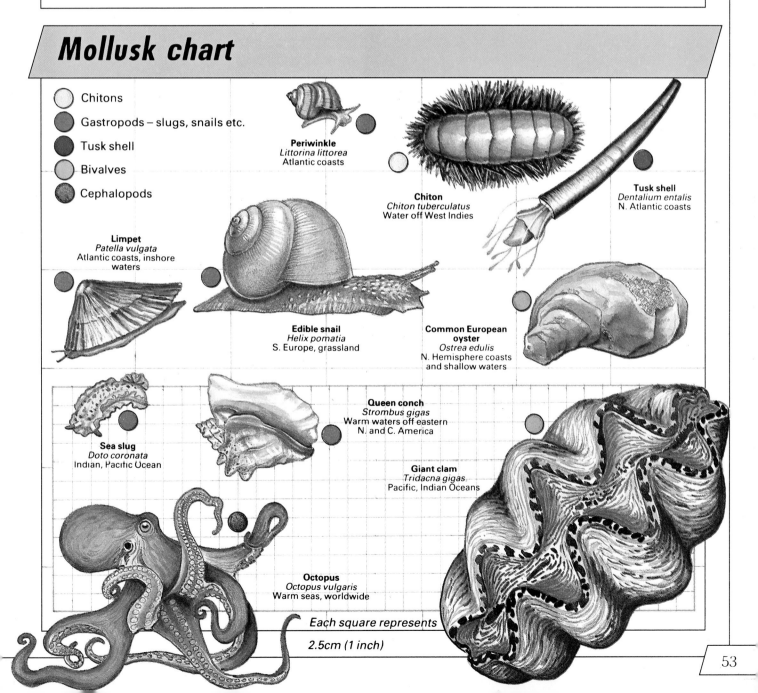

○ Chitons

● Gastropods – slugs, snails etc.

● Tusk shell

○ Bivalves

● Cephalopods

Periwinkle
Littorina littorea
Atlantic coasts

Chiton
Chiton tuberculatus
Water off West Indies

Tusk shell
Dentalium entalis
N. Atlantic coasts

Limpet
Patella vulgata
Atlantic coasts, inshore
waters

Edible snail
Helix pomatia
S. Europe, grassland

**Common European
oyster**
Ostrea edulis
N. Hemisphere coasts
and shallow waters

Sea slug
Doto coronata
Indian, Pacific Ocean

Queen conch
Strombus gigas
Warm waters off eastern
N. and C. America

Giant clam
Tridacna gigas
Pacific, Indian Oceans

Octopus
Octopus vulgaris
Warm seas, worldwide

Each square represents

2.5cm (1 inch)

ARTHROPODS

Major types:
Crustaceans, such as shrimps, crabs, lobsters, barnacles, woodlice (25,000 species).
King crabs (5).
Arachnids, including spiders, scorpions, mites (53,000).
Millipedes (8,000).
Centipedes (2,000).
Insects, including flies, dragonflies, cockroaches, ants, termites, beetles, lice, fleas and bees (800,000).

Arthropod means joint-legged, and most present-day kinds of these invertebrates evolved from earthworm-like animals that had a pair of limbs to each body segment. Four out of every five animals alive on Earth today are arthropods which include insects, spiders, crabs, ticks and millipedes. They each have a body divided into a series of similar segments and encased in a horny layer, the cuticle. The cuticle is usually rigid and tough and forms an external protective covering, the exoskeleton. This thin tubular skeleton gives greater strength for its weight than a solid rod-like skeleton like humans'. Between them arthropods inhabit land, water and air throughout the world.

Breathing

Spiders, scorpions and many other land arthropods breathe through internal feathery gill-like structures called book-lungs. Species fully adapted to life in water, such as lobsters, crayfish and crabs, have internal gills like those of fish and draw water into the gill chamber where an exchange of oxygen (dissolved in the water) and waste carbon dioxide takes place. Insects have a system of tubes, the tracheae, through which air can circulate or, in some beetles, is actively pumped by air sacs near the spiracles. From the main tracheae, the air flows through smaller trachioles to muscles and organs. This breathing system is efficient but relies mainly on the free movement of air which is possible over short distances only. This limits the size of insects to only a few centimeters in length.

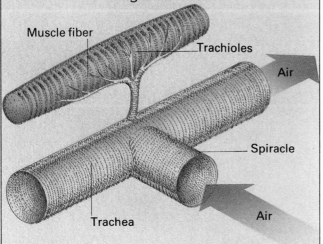

Muscle fiber
Trachioles
Air
Spiracle
Trachea
Air

Brain
A pair of nerve swellings, or ganglia, act as a brain and connect to the various sense organs. A nerve cord extends from the ganglia along the animal's lower surface.

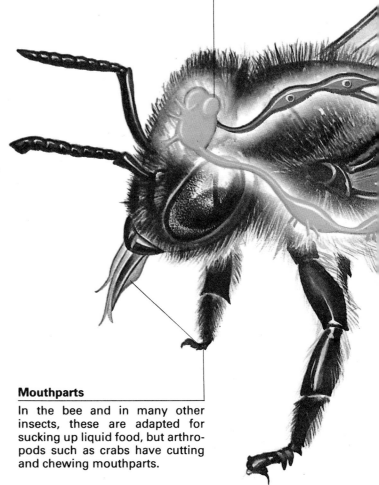

Mouthparts
In the bee and in many other insects, these are adapted for sucking up liquid food, but arthropods such as crabs have cutting and chewing mouthparts.

Wings

Most insects have two pairs of wings. These are linked by a flexible portion of exoskeleton on top of the body, and are strengthened by the pressure of blood forced into a network of veins running through them. Pairs of muscles contract and relax alternately to flex the link-piece, which in turn moves the wings up and down.

Body plan

Arthropods are bilaterally symmetrical – that is the left and right sides are identical. In addition, the body is divided into front, middle and hind portions. In the honey bee this is visible as the head, thorax and abdomen regions. In crustaceans such as crayfish, the head and thorax appear as a single unit, the cephalothorax. In insects, jointed limbs and wings are carried on segments of the thorax.

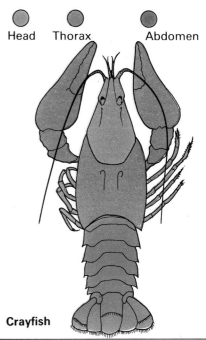

Head   Thorax   Abdomen

Crayfish

Heart

Instead of one large heart and major blood vessels (as in a mammal), there is usually a ribbon of small heart chambers that runs down the body and open blood spaces, the haemocoels.

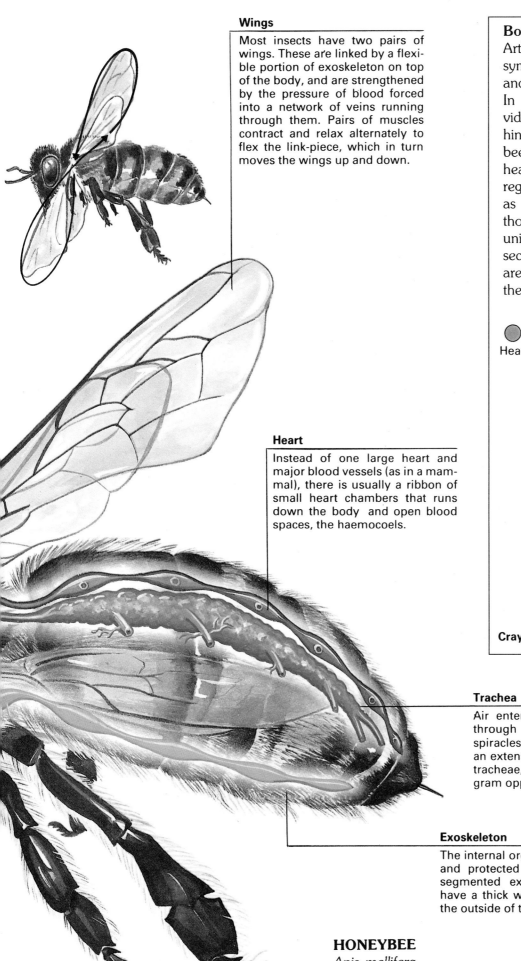

Trachea

Air enters and leaves the body through holes on each side, the spiracles, and is pumped through an extensive system of tubes, the tracheae, to all parts. (See diagram opposite).

Exoskeleton

The internal organs are contained and protected within the tough segmented exoskeleton. Insects have a thick waterproof layer on the outside of the exoskeleton.

HONEYBEE
Apis mellifera

CRUSTACEANS

Major types:
Branchiopods (1,200 species), the freshwater shrimps and water fleas.
Copepods (4,500) are tiny aquatic species that form most of the animal plankton.
Barnacles (800), as adults, attach themselves to rocks, ships or other marine animals.
Shrimps, lobsters, crabs and woodlice (18,000).

Ranging in size from the 4m (13ft) span Japanese spider crab to tiny water fleas, and including lobsters, woodlice and barnacles, are a group of arthropods known as crustaceans. Most live in sea or fresh water and breathe through gills. Land species such as woodlice have specialized gills or breathe through the body surface, but this needs moisture and so the animals are confined to damp habitats. A typical crustacean, for example a lobster, has a large plate of skeleton, the carapace, over the thorax, and has a pair of legs or other appendages on each segment of its body. Its life cycle involves fertilized eggs that develop into larvae that are quite unlike the adults.

Feeding

Branchiopod, or gill-leg, crustaceans such as water fleas are filter feeders. By swinging their legs forward, they draw in water between them and filter off food particles. They then swing their legs back and this washes the food to their mouthpart limbs, which direct it into the mouth. Crabs and lobsters are scavengers, feeding on the remains of fish and marine animals. Their first pair of legs are adapted as nipping claws and their mouthparts are able to crush and chew chunks of animal food. Woodlice, or pill bugs, eat dead leaves and wood.

A deep-sea prawn feeds on particles in the water.

Growth

To grow bigger, an arthropod must shed its old exoskeleton and grow a new and larger one to replace it. During this period of molting the animal lacks support and is vulnerable to predators. When a crab is ready to molt, body tissues linked to the carapace break, and the animal hunches itself up and slowly withdraws, abdomen first. The new skeleton quickly hardens. This life-long ability to grow new tissues allows many crustaceans to regrow parts such as claws and mouthparts that have been injured or lost to enemies such as squid.

An edible crab shedding its shell

Life cycle

In most species the sexes are separate and individuals develop from eggs laid by the female following mating and fertilization. In aquatic species especially, fertilized eggs develop into a series of larvae. The first of these is similar in all species of crustaceans and is quite unlike the adults, with an oval body and three pairs of limbs. Freshwater branchiopods such as brine shrimps and water fleas produce heavily-shelled eggs that can withstand drought and cold. Pond water fleas can, in favorable conditions, produce offspring without fertilization of eggs.

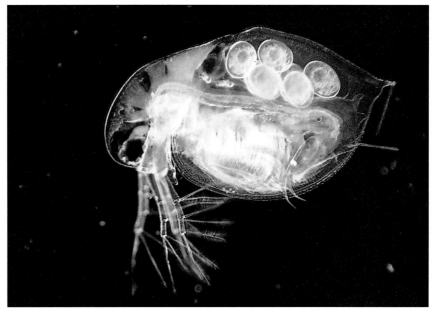
A water flea carries eggs inside her brood pouch.

Defense and protection

In addition to providing support, the exoskeleton gives arthropods varying degrees of defense against predators, parasites and disease-causing bacteria and viruses. The exoskeleton is composed largely of a carbohydrate, or sugar, type of chemical called chitin, but in crustaceans it is heavily impregnated with calcium salts for extra hardness. The carapace of lobsters and crabs is particularly strengthened in this way. In some land-living crustaceans such as woodlice, the armored exoskeleton is so jointed that the animal can roll itself up into a ball as protection against predators such as spiders. A waxy coating on the skeleton prevents water loss.

The mud lobster has a hard protective carapace.

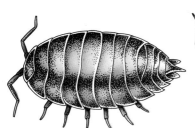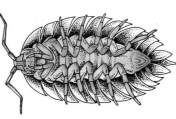
To protect itself the woodlouse rolls up into an armor plated ball.

ARACHNIDS AND KING CRABS

Spiders, scorpions and their relatives the ticks and mites (a group called arachnids), are probably the most disliked of arthropods because some tropical species have nasty poisonous bites, and many ticks, as skin parasites, produce unpleasant rashes and sometimes transmit deadly diseases. Most of these animals live on land, breathe using book-lungs, and are aggressive predators, preying on other small arthropods. Spiders, for example, are insects' greatest enemies. Unlike insects, they do not have antennae, and their mouthparts always include a pair of chelicerae, or fangs, that carry poison ducts, and pedipalps, or jaws. King crabs have walking legs and pincers like true crabs, but resemble spiders.

Structure

The basic plan of arachnids is a segmented body divided into two sections, a combined head and thorax or cephalothorax, and the abdomen. The joint with the body is narrow like a neck. The specialized mouthparts are followed by four pairs of long, jointed walking legs. In spiders the rear of the abdomen bears six silk-producing glands, the spinnerets, and in scorpions it carries a poisonous spine used to paralyze prey. Arachnids have simple eyes rather than the complex, compound eyes of most insects, and do not rely greatly on vision to catch prey. But their sense organs do include hair-like projections of the cuticle that are sensitive to touch and vibrations. In aquatic species such as water spiders, these are also used to trap a film of air that is taken under water to a breathing bell of silk attached to water plants. This enables them to stay under water.

A female wolf spider

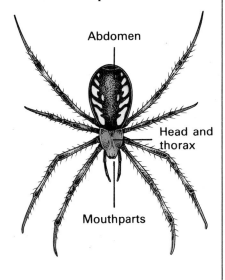

Abdomen

Head and thorax

Mouthparts

Parasites

There are many free-living ticks and mites that inhabit leaf litter and are involved in the breakdown of animal and plant remains in the soil. Most, though, are parasites and are found in large numbers on the surface of hosts that include fish, domestic animals and people. Ticks suck blood, and some mites hitch a lift on insects to move between food sources.

Harvestman infested with mites

Webs

Spiders that use silk to catch prey employ it as trip-wires, lassos or webs. Silk is spun as a thread from the spinnerets. Orb spiders produce a circular web and sit in the middle of this waiting for an insect to get caught in sticky drops on the threads. As the first stage in making the web, the spider spins a long thread which will then be blown by the wind to a nearby support (1). Having made this bridge thread, it crosses it, lays down a second thread (2), then pulls this into a V-shape (3). With the frame complete, the spider adds arms, or radii, to make a platform in the middle (4). It then forms spiral threads (5) and completes the web (6).

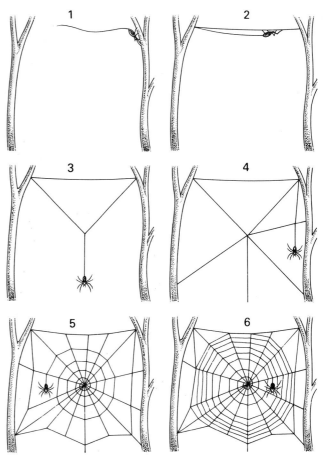

An orb spider wrapping its prey in silk

Breathing

King crabs live on or near shores of North America and much of Southeast Asia. Like spiders, scorpions and most other arachnids, they breathe through book-lungs. In spiders these are gill-like structures made up of leaves, like the pages of a book, each containing circulating blood and in contact with air drawn into the lung chamber. King crabs have five pairs of book-lungs, each consisting of as many as 200 thin leaves. They are adapted for breathing in water so whenever these arthropods come out to the beach, as they do to breed, they must keep the book-lungs moist. This they do by plowing along in the sand. In the water, king crabs swim along upside down flapping the book-lungs, an action that circulates water among the lung leaves.

A king crab has six pairs of limbs.

Feeding

Most arachnids feed on animal food, which they can only take in liquid form. They must therefore kill or stun their prey then pump it full of digestive juices before sucking out the semi-digested contents. Scorpions are limited to the warm regions of the world. They feed mainly at night, capturing insects with their pincers then using their sting to poison or paralyze the prey. Harvestmen, which look like long-legged spiders, live in low-growing vegetation and as well as hunting small invertebrates, also eat dead animal and plant material. Parasitic ticks and mites have mouthparts adapted for piercing and clinging to the host's outer surface and for sucking up blood or, in the case of plant parasites, sap. Most do not kill their host unless they infect them with germs that they carry. Among spiders, many construct webs to trap flying insects. The web may be circular and elegantly built, funnel-shaped, or just a formless tangle of silk threads. Raft spiders hunt on water by detecting surface vibrations made by insects such as mosquitoes. Tropical trapdoor spiders live in an underground burrow and as an insect passes by, flap open the hinged cover of the burrow and pounce. Wolf spiders chase prey, and jumping spiders stalk and pounce. South American tarantulas, or bird-eating spiders, prey on small birds and reptiles but usually eat invertebrates. King crabs gather small worms and shellfish from the seabed.

An Australian scorpion killing a cricket

A trapdoor spider emerges from its lair

A water spider with a dead fly in its 'larder'

Mating

Spiders have the most elaborate mating system among arachnids. The male spins a small web, deposits his sperm on it, then sucks up the sperm into special storage organs near his mouth. He then goes in search of a mate. The male courts the female in one of many ways. He may use a visual display, waving his legs about to signal he carries sperm. Or he may touch her, present her with food gift wrapped in silk, or vibrate her web in a special way. During mating the male inserts his pedipalps into the female's sperm-storing organs and deposits sufficient sperm to fertilize several batches of eggs. After mating the male often dies, usually through exhaustion although female black widow spiders of North America devour their mate, which is much smaller in size.

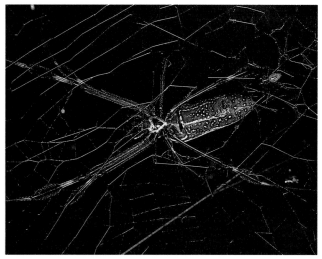

A female spider and her tiny mate

Offspring

Female spiders lay several batches of eggs each year and enclose each batch with a silken cocoon or covering. The common European garden spider, for example, may lay ten batches of 1,000 or more eggs each. The cocoons can often be seen on garden plants in late summer. Some female spiders bury the cocoons in soil and leave the offspring to fend for themselves. Several tropical species guard the eggs from insect predators or, as in wolf spiders, carry them around on their back. Young spiderlings hatch in the cocoons and a few days later emerge. They allow themselves to be dispersed by the wind. They then go through several molts before reaching adult size and acquiring fully formed eyes, spinnerets and claws on their legs. Scorpions produce large numbers of live young, which the female initially carries around on her back.

A mother scorpion carrying her 28 babies

INSECTS

Numbering more than 800,000 species, insects have colonized the world more widely than any other group of animals. They are absent only from deep-sea water. Some such as fleas and lice, are parasites of mammals. Although some carry disease, and others are major pests of crops, insects are important as pollinators and recyclers. High-flying species form an aerial plankton on which many birds depend for food. As arthropods, they have a segmented, three-section body. The head bears specialized sense organs, the antennae, and the thorax has three pairs of walking legs and usually two pairs of wings. The abdomen often has jointed structures adapted for mating or stinging.

Life cycle

Insects can be divided into two distinct groups based on the type of offspring that emerge from the females' fertilized eggs. Among wingless insects and the most primitive winged species, such as earwigs and locusts, the eggs hatch into young that closely resemble the adults. The young are often called nymphs. All other insects produce eggs that hatch into larvae, which are quite unlike the adults and usually feed on entirely different food. A female gnat, for example, lays eggs as a raft on water. After a few days these hatch into larvae that breathe air at the surface through special tracheal tubes and feed on microscopic algae in the water. Each larva then changes into a pre-adult stage, the pupa. This too breathes air but does not feed. Finally, the pupal skin splits open and the young adult, flying insect emerges, and the cycle continues. Adult male gnats feed on nectar, and females on the blood of birds or small mammals.

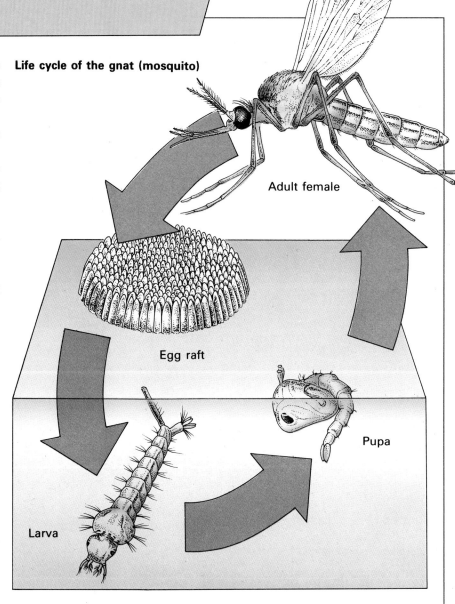

Life cycle of the gnat (mosquito)

Adult female

Egg raft

Larva

Pupa

Flying

True flies, called dipterans, have just one pair of flying wings. So too do cockroaches and beetles and their allies, the cockchafers and ladybirds, although they also have a pair of non-flying wings that are modified to form protective wing covers, the elytra. Species with two pairs of flying wings include butterflies and moths, mayflies, and dragonflies. Some dragonflies can fly at speeds of 100 kph (65mph).

A seven-spot ladybird flying to a flower

Jumping

Springtails have a special forked structure on their abdomen that acts like a spring and enables them to jump. Fleas, crickets and grasshoppers jump by folding up then quickly extending their long powerful hindlegs. Fleas can jump more than 30cm (12in) high. As wingless insects, this is an adaptation to their way of life. Female fleas lay their eggs on the ground, and the adults that develop from the larvae have to be able to leap in the air to attach to a host animal.

Flea

Walking and swimming

Aquatic insects include water boatmen, or backswimmers, water skaters or rovers, and water beetles. Backswimmers are so called because they often turn upside-down and, using their large third pair of legs as oars, swim along. When diving they carry down a store of air trapped between bristles on their body. The skaters skim over the surface of ponds and lakes, using their middle legs like oars and their hind legs to steer. Water beetles live as larvae and adults in fresh water. They stay afloat by keeping a bubble of air under their wing covers. All these aquatic invertebrates are carnivorous, feeding on tadpoles, aquatic worms and small fish.

Insects that scurry across solid surfaces use their legs in a highly coordinated walking action. The legs on each side of the body are moved in sequence from back to front. Cockroaches, for example, when walking slowly move the legs on one side, then on the other.

Millipedes, and other arthropods have more legs.

A pond skater walking on water

Offense and defense

Fleas and lice have a tough, leathery skin to prevent injury from the host's scratching. As protection against damage or injury to their wings, members of the beetle family characteristically have elytra. In many ladybirds and cockchafers the elytra are brightly colored to act as a warning to predators, especially birds. Bombardier beetles actively defend themselves by squirting a foul smelling fluid from the end of their abdomen. Similarly many ants squirt formic acid at their enemies, and bees and wasps use their tail sting. Honeybees have a sting equipped with projections, or barbs, so that they cannot pull it out of their attacker and use it again. Bumblebees and wasps can use their sting many times over. Stick and leaf insects resemble the twigs, blades of grass or leaves on which they rest, and tropical tree hoppers are bugs that have bizarre extensions of the thorax believed to function as camouflage. Some caterpillars, the larvae of butterflies and moths, have prickly spines as deterrents, and others, such as the puss moth caterpillar, are well camouflaged but when threatened rear up to expose vivid eye spots or facial markings. These frighten off most would-be attackers. Many other insects have eye spots on their wings to deter birds and small mammals, and are also foul tasting. Other butterfly species have, during evolution, acquired similar markings but are pleasant to eat. Because they resemble, or mimic, the nasty-tasting species, they are not eaten as readily.

A stick insect looks just like a twig.

A silkmoth caterpillar has poisonous spines.

An io moth's eye spots frighten attackers.

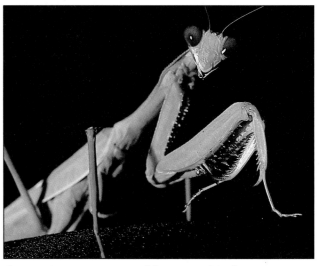
A praying mantis resembles part of a plant.

Feeding

The mouthparts of insects show adaptations to a wide variety of diets. Locusts and leaf insects have mouthparts that can bite and chew plant food. Butterflies and moths have a pair of especially long mouthparts that are joined together by hooks and spines to form a tube, the proboscis, through which the insects suck up nectar. When not in use, the proboscis is coiled up like a clock spring. Bees, too, feed on nectar, and have a special extendible tube that leads from the mouth to a nectar store in the thorax. Houseflies suck up liquid food that usually consists of animal remains. Horseflies, though, use their mouthparts like a sponge to take up blood. Lice and fleas pierce the hosts' skin and suck up blood. Preying mantises have strong chewing mouthparts with which they devour other insects. Aphids feed on the sap of plants but in turn are preyed upon by ladybirds. Hunting wasps live alone and prey mostly on caterpillars. A female paralyzes a caterpillar using her tail sting, drags it to a breeding nest and lays an egg on it. When the larva hatches, it feeds on the caterpillar.

A parasitic wasp lays an egg on a living caterpillar.

A carnivorous dragonfly nymph eating the tadpole of a frog

Senses

An insect's sensory equipment includes a pair of antennae, which can detect smell and in some cases vibrations, and a pair of compound eyes. The eyes consist of thousands of identical optical units packed closely together and linked to the brain via nerves. Each unit is made up of a lens-and-cone system that directs light on to a transparent rod, the rhabdom, which is surrounded by light-sensitive nerve cells. When these are stimulated, they send messages to the insect's brain. The units can record the presence or absence of light, its strength, and in most cases, its color, forming a mosaic image.

The compound eyes of a deer fly

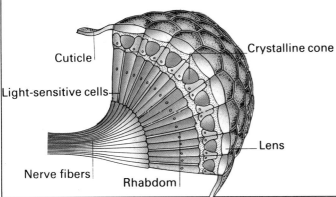

Cuticle

Crystalline cone

Light-sensitive cells

Lens

Nerve fibers

Rhabdom

Parasites

Bugs, fleas and lice are the most common parasitic insects. Many are of economic importance, causing damage to crops and spreading plant and animal diseases, for example the bubonic plague of rats and people. Other parasitic insects include tropical earwigs that live in rats' fur.

Lice live on warm-blooded animals. A host such as a sheep may harbor many thousands of several species. Some pierce the host's skin and suck up blood. Others chew the host's feathers, hair or dead skin cells, but also feed on blood produced by the host's scratching. Fleas have a similar lifestyle to sucking lice. Among bugs, species such as the assassin bugs that are found in all warm places are parasites of other insects, while shield, or stink bugs are serious parasites of plants in semi-tropical regions. Probably the most widespread of the plant-feeding bugs are the sap-feeding aphids.

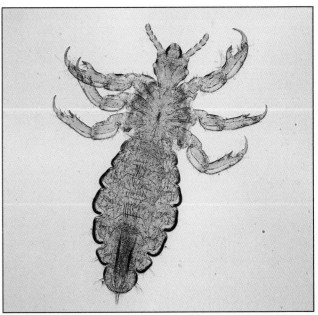
The head louse lives in humans' hair

Mating

Female moths produce chemicals known as pheromones to attract the males (which detect them with their antennae). Among dragonflies and damselflies, the male grasps the female with claspers at the end of his abdomen, then inserts his sperm into her.

Damselflies mating on a blade of grass

Eggs

The success of insects results from the many thousands of eggs females lay each year. Also species such as aphids can reproduce without fertilization of the eggs. In a year, a single aphid could, theoretically give rise to a population of many billions.

A harlequin bug guarding its eggs

Metamorphosis

Flies, butterflies and mosquitoes have a life cycle typical of highly evolved insects. After mating, the female lays her eggs on or near food suitable for the larvae that will hatch. The larval stage, consisting of a grub or caterpillar, is one in which the insect grows rapidly by continuous feeding. The change, or metamorphosis, of the larva to the adult takes place via a resting stage, the pupa or chrysalis. This is when wings and associated muscles develop and, in butterflies and moths especially, mouthparts change from a leaf-chewing to a nectar-sucking apparatus. During the adult stage, the insects break out of the chrysalis. They disperse to avoid overcrowding, and reproduce, continuing the life cycle.

A red admiral butterfly emerging from its chrysalis

Social life

Bees, wasps, ants and termites are often called social insects because many of them have a lifestyle in which individuals live together in colonies. The colony home of African termites can reach 6m (20ft) tall, and a beehive can contain 100,000 bees. Within a colony there are workers and soldiers, which are specialized to collect food and defend the home, and reproductive males and females. Individuals communicate with each other using chemical signals or, as in honeybees, displays on the honeycomb in the hive. Usually each colony dies out at the end of the year, but not before producing a queen bee and males to fertilize her.

Worker bees on a honeycomb

Weaver ants make a nest of leaves.

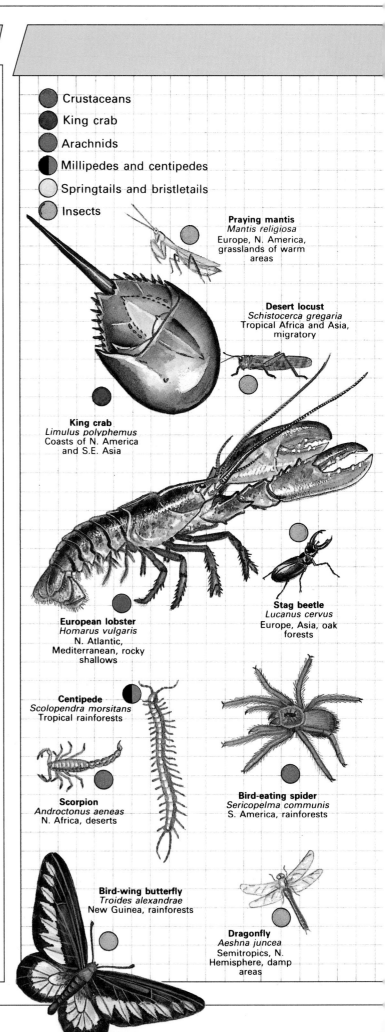

- Crustaceans
- King crab
- Arachnids
- Millipedes and centipedes
- Springtails and bristletails
- Insects

Praying mantis
Mantis religiosa
Europe, N. America, grasslands of warm areas

Desert locust
Schistocerca gregaria
Tropical Africa and Asia, migratory

King crab
Limulus polyphemus
Coasts of N. America and S.E. Asia

European lobster
Homarus vulgaris
N. Atlantic, Mediterranean, rocky shallows

Stag beetle
Lucanus cervus
Europe, Asia, oak forests

Centipede
Scolopendra morsitans
Tropical rainforests

Scorpion
Androctonus aeneas
N. Africa, deserts

Bird-eating spider
Sericopelma communis
S. America, rainforests

Bird-wing butterfly
Troides alexandrae
New Guinea, rainforests

Dragonfly
Aeshna juncea
Semitropics, N. Hemisphere, damp areas

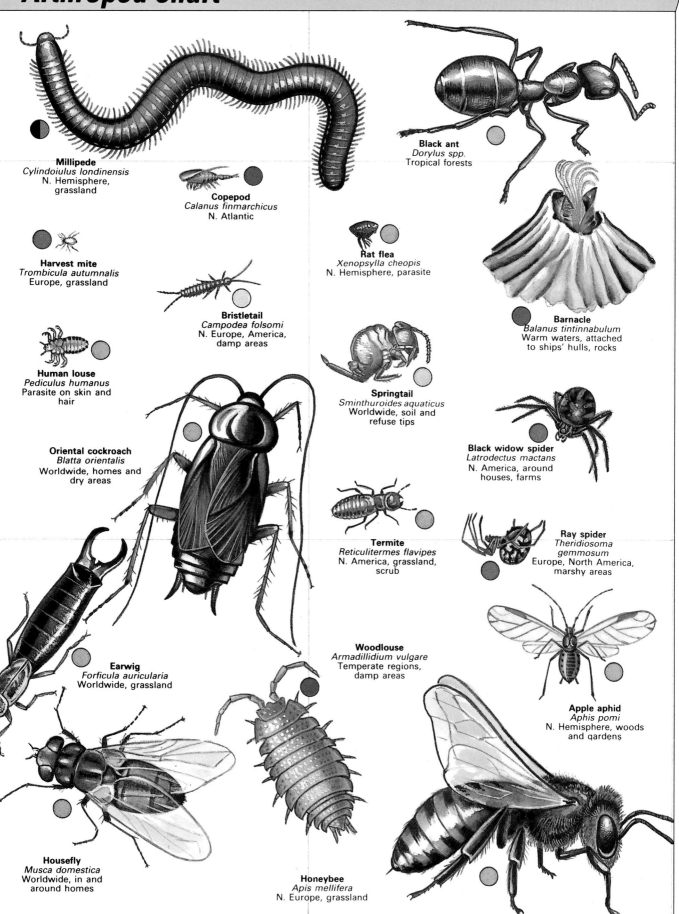

Millipede
Cylindoiulus londinensis
N. Hemisphere,
grassland

Copepod
Calanus finmarchicus
N. Atlantic

Harvest mite
Trombicula autumnalis
Europe, grassland

Bristletail
Campodea folsomi
N. Europe, America,
damp areas

Human louse
Pediculus humanus
Parasite on skin and
hair

Oriental cockroach
Blatta orientalis
Worldwide, homes and
dry areas

Earwig
Forficula auricularia
Worldwide, grassland

Housefly
Musca domestica
Worldwide, in and
around homes

Black ant
Dorylus spp.
Tropical forests

Rat flea
Xenopsylla cheopis
N. Hemisphere, parasite

Barnacle
Balanus tintinnabulum
Warm waters, attached
to ships' hulls, rocks

Springtail
Sminthuroides aquaticus
Worldwide, soil and
refuse tips

Black widow spider
Latrodectus mactans
N. America, around
houses, farms

Termite
Reticulitermes flavipes
N. America, grassland,
scrub

Ray spider
*Theridiosoma
gemmosum*
Europe, North America,
marshy areas

Woodlouse
Armadillidium vulgare
Temperate regions,
damp areas

Apple aphid
Aphis pomi
N. Hemisphere, woods
and gardens

Honeybee
Apis mellifera
N. Europe, grassland

Each square represents 2.5cm (1 inch)

FISH TO REPTILES

CONTENTS

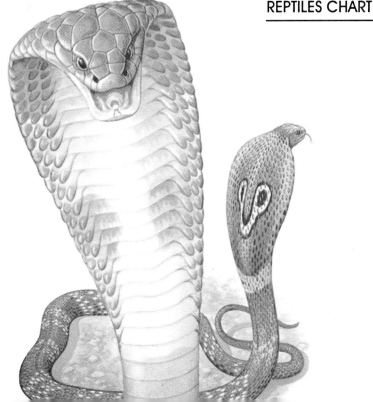

INTRODUCTION

In biological terms, fish are the simplest and most numerous vertebrate (backboned) animals. They were also the first vertebrates to evolve, nearly 500 million years ago. Like their invertebrate ancestors, fish spend their entire lives in water. But because nearly three-quarters of the Earth is covered with water, they have more available living space than all the other animals in the world. Fish have used this space to evolve a tremendous variety of forms, from tiny species a few millimeters long which dart among tropical coral to the enormous 18.5m (61 ft) whale shark.

Amphibians, such as frogs and toads, which evolved about 280 million years ago, still have to return to water to lay their eggs, but as adults most have legs and live on the land. They usually have to keep their bodies moist. Reptiles also lay eggs, but they are protected by a leathery shell and are laid on land. Even aquatic reptiles, such as turtles, come ashore to lay their eggs. They are cold-blooded, so they are restricted to warm climates. Most walk on four legs although one large group – the snakes– have become legless and have to slither along on the ground.

FISH

There are about 25,000 different species or kinds of fish, which is more than all the other backboned animals put together. They range in size from tiny gobies less than 10mm (0.4 in) long to whale sharks up to 18.5m (61 ft) in length and weighing 43 tons. All are adapted for living in the water. They are found everywhere, from the icy waters of the polar regions to tropical lakes and swamps. They are cold-blooded and breathe through gills. Most have streamlined bodies for moving quickly through the water. They use their tails to push forward and have several pairs or sets of fins to help steer and keep themselves upright.

Classification: 4 major classes – cartilaginous fish, bony fish, jawless fish and lungfish.
Commonest species: 10cm (4 in) long deep-sea bristlemouth, which preys on small crustaceans.
Rarest species: probably the coelacanth, a 2m (6ft) long offshore species, once thought to be extinct.
Lifespan: from about 6 months (small tropical species) to 85 years (sturgeon).

Gills
These special breathing organs are usually protected by a tough gill-cover, the operculum.

BROWN TROUT
Salmo trutta

Brain
The areas of the brain dealing with smell and muscle control are highly developed.

Skeleton
Most fish have a bony jointed backbone, the vertebral column, and a skull encasing the brain.

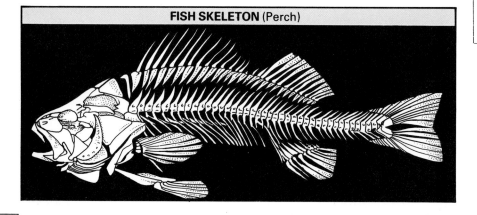

FISH SKELETON (Perch)

Heart
This muscular organ pumps blood around the animal's body. It is protected by bones that support the pectoral fins.

Skin
The outer protective covering of most fish bears thin, overlapping tiny scales.

Blood circulation/The heart

Fish have a two-chambered heart. Deoxygenated blood (blue) is pumped around the body and chamber, the ventricle, to the gills where it is refreshed. This oxygenated blood (red) is then pumped round the body and returns to the heart's collecting chamber, the atrium, deoxygenated.

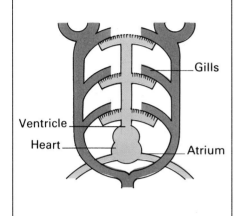

Gills

Ventricle

Heart

Atrium

Nerve cord

Protected within the backbone, the nerve cord relays messages between the brain and the rest of the body.

Breathing in water

Water out through opercular slit

Operculum

Gill filaments

Gill bars

Oxygenated blood to head and body

Water in through mouth

Gill filaments

Blood capillaries

Direction of water flow

Deoxygenated blood pumped to gills by heart

In fish, sets of gills lie on each side of the head. Each gill is strengthened by a bony or gristle bar and is divided into many filaments. As the fish opens its mouth, water containing oxygen is drawn in. The water is pumped across the gills to the chamber behind the operculum. Blood flowing in capillaries within the gills is full of unwanted carbon dioxide and poor in oxygen (deoxygenated). An exchange of carbon dioxide and oxygen takes place between the deoxygenated blood and the fresh water. The gill blood becomes refreshed (oxygenated), and the water, now full of carbon dioxide, flows away as the fish closes its mouth. This water is pushed out of an opening at the back of the operculum.

SHARKS, SKATES AND RAYS

Classification: 3 main classes – sharks and dogfish (210 species), skates and rays (300 species) and chimaeras or ratfish (20 species).
Evolution: evolved some 345 million years ago from "plate-skinned" fish.
Most dangerous to people: 6m (20ft) Great White shark.

Probably the most fearsome of fish are the sharks, rays and their relatives. Most inhabit warm seas. They have skeletons made of cartilage or gristle instead of bone, and their skin contains small sharp scales coated with an enamel that is similar to that of mammalian teeth. They have to keep moving to circulate water over the gills in order to extract oxygen to breathe. All have a mouth adapted for biting, with a set of teeth attached to the upper and lower jaw. However, while most of these cartilaginous fish are meat-eaters, others feed on plankton, the tiny animals and plants that float in surface waters. The strange electric rays, or torpedo fish, can generate an electric current to sting prey.

Feeding

The aptly named tiger shark seizes its prey.

Flesh-eating sharks mainly hunt and eat fish, but they are also scavengers and feed on dead animals. Only rarely do they attack people, and then it is usually because they have been provoked or they have smelled blood. Their teeth point backwards so that when they catch a fish it cannot escape however hard it wriggles. The two largest species, the whale shark and the basking shark, are plankton-feeders and are harmless. They have small teeth and sieve their food from the water as it is taken in through the mouth using gill rakers. Skates and rays show similar varied feeding habits.

Swimming

A manta ray swims by flapping its "wings".

Most fish swim by producing sideways flapping movements of their body and tail. Cartilaginous fish have two sets of paired fins that extend each side of the body, and various single fins above and below the mid-line. Unlike bony fish, they do not possess an air-filled swim bladder to help stay afloat, so most species stay swimming at all times to avoid sinking. They therefore never sleep, but they do take short rest periods. Skates and rays have flatter bodies and stay near the sea bed. Their large "wings" are enlarged fins, which they use to keep stable in the water and to push themselves along.

Reproduction

Most sharks, skates and rays produce live young. Along the inner edge of the male's rear paired fins are tube-like structures, called claspers, which the male fish uses to deposit sperm inside the female. Eggs in the female are fertilized by the sperm and develop into tiny embryos. Eventually, the young fish are released into the water. Some female skates, rays and sharks lay their eggs in horny capsules, (or purses, which they deposit in sand in shallow water or attached to seaweed). This provides protection for the embryos, which take months to hatch. The empty egg cases, called mermaid's purses, can be found washed up on beaches.

Catshark embryos develop inside egg cases.

Senses

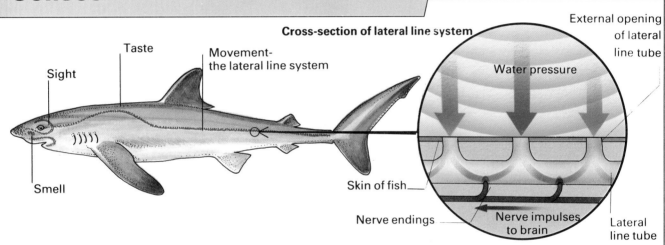

Cross-section of lateral line system

Sight

Taste

Movement-
the lateral line system

Smell

Water pressure

External opening of lateral line tube

Skin of fish

Nerve endings

Nerve impulses to brain

Lateral line tube

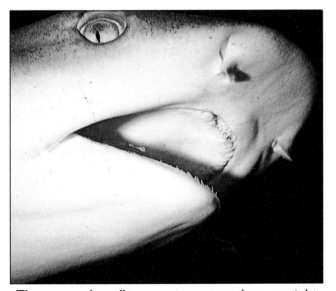
The sense of smell is more important than eyesight.

Few sharks and rays have a keen sense of vision, and most do not rely on this sense for locating food or finding their way about. All cartilaginous fish have very well-developed and sensitive senses of smell, balance and noise detection. Running along each side of the body and within the head is a network of fluid-filled tubes. This is the lateral line system which contains sense organs that are sensitive to pressure waves in the water. When the sense organs are triggered, their nerves send messages to the brain, where they are interpreted. As the fish swims along it can detect the movement of other fish and detect the difference between the motion of a healthy fish swimming nearby and the movements of an easy-to-catch injured fish struggling in the water. Their sense of smell can also detect blood in the water.

Partnerships

Remora suckerfish hitch a ride on a reef shark.

Various parasites live on the skin of fish. Other unrelated fish feed on these unwelcome animals and pieces of dead skin and are known as cleaners. The cleaners of sharks and rays are fortunate in rarely being eaten by the hosts and some, such as the remoras, who cling on using a sucker on their head, are carried around by the sharks. Pilot fish also form partnerships with sharks and rays, acting as cleaners or feeding on scraps from the shark's meal.

Weapons

Chimaeras, or ratfish, are related to sharks and rays. Like them, they have small gill covers and most live in deep oceans. They have long slender tails and at the front of their first upper fin is a poisonous sharp spine to fend off attackers.

Some rays, known as torpedo fish, have highly developed organs which can discharge a large electric current that is the same strength as household electricity supplies. They use the electric shock to stun prey.

A ratfish's poisonous spine deters attackers.

The electric ray stuns its prey using electricity.

JAWLESS FISH

Classification: one order of 50 species.
Evolution: modern representatives evolved some 270 million years ago from "shell-skinned" fish.
Common species: glutinous Atlantic hagfish and the sea lamprey.

The earliest vertebrate animals to have evolved are today represented by the hagfish and lampreys. These are generally known as jawless fish or round-mouths. They are parasites and scavengers, and instead of proper jaws have thin, horny structures surrounding a sucker-like mouth. Like eels, they do not have paired fins, and their skin is smooth, slimy and lacks scales. There are about 50 different species. Some lampreys live in the sea, others in rivers and streams, where they latch on to other fish and suck their blood, injecting a chemical that prevents blood clotting. Hagfish live in the sea, scavenging on the flesh of dead and dying fish.

Lifestyle

The primitive hagfish resembles an eel and has remained virtually unchanged from its ancestors of 500 million years ago. Hagfish live on the sea bottom, burrowing in the sand or mud during the day and scavenging for dead and dying fish or catching worms and crustaceans at night. Unlike all other fish they have no lower jaw. They use their rasp-like tongue to bore into the flesh of prey. Most species are blind and hunt by touch and smell. As adults, the jawless lampreys attach themselves to other fish, such as trout, using their sucker. They rasp away at the host's flesh with their teeth, then suck its blood. The adults breed in fresh water. The female lays the fertilized eggs in the gravel of stream- or riverbeds. Then, together with her mate, she dies. The larvae spend several years buried in river mud before finally emerging as adults. They sometimes reach plague proportions in American rivers and do great damage to fish.

An Atlantic lamprey's teeth-lined sucker mouth

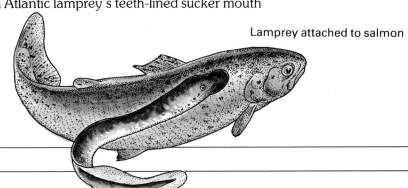

Lamprey attached to salmon

BONY FISH (Lakes and ponds)

Major groups: pikes, carp, sticklebacks, minnows, swamp eels, perch and lungfish.
Largest species: Nile perch – weighs up to 180kg (400lbs).
Smallest species: Dwarf pigmy goby – less than 10mm (0.4 inches) long, weight about 4mg (0.15 ounce).
Longest lived: Lake sturgeon – up to 85 years.

Fish with skeletons consisting of bone are the most numerous of all, and of these several thousand species spend their entire lives in freshwater lakes and ponds. They are able to survive in a natural world that is isolated from others and is constantly changing in temperature and nutrient levels. Some swim just below the surface, feeding on plankton or plants that grow at the water's edge. Others lurk in deep water, eating worms, insects and amphibian larvae. The most varied populations are often found in freshwater lakes or large ponds where there is plenty of food. Some pond fish grow to a very large size. Japanese golden carp, for example, weigh as much as 36kg (80 lbs).

Breeding

Most fish living in the calm waters of lakes and ponds produce eggs that remain submerged and usually attached to plants or buried in the sand or mud at the bottom. This peaceful habitat has also helped the evolution of elaborate breeding systems among fish, as in the three-spined stickleback of North America and Eurasia. The male defends a territory from other male sticklebacks, builds a nest for the eggs, attracts a female and mates with her. He flaps his fins to make the female lay eggs and then looks after the young fish.

A male stickleback stimulates a female to lay eggs.

Breathing

Many fish that live in slimy, stagnant water, or in ponds, lakes or swamps that sometimes dry out, can breathe with their gills but they also have lungs. True lungfish live in tropical swamps of Africa, Australia and South America. Some can survive total drying out. While the swamp is still damp, the fish burrows into the mud and forms a protective cocoon lined with mucus from its body. Obtaining air through tiny holes in the lid of the burrow and living on reserves of fat, it can survive until the next rainy season.

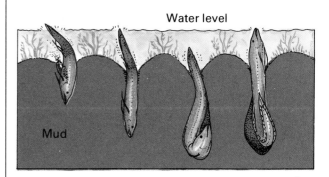

Water level

Mud

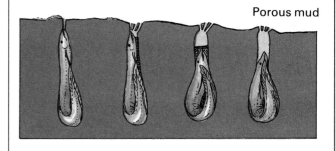

Porous mud

Food chains

The number and types of fish that live in a lake or pond largely depend on the food available and predators present. A diagram showing what eats what is known as a food web. For a fresh-water habitat such as a temperate lake, the web shows that some fish depend on plankton and invertebrates for their meals, and others on fish relatives. Such a food web starts with detritus and phytoplankton. Detritus consists of the remains of dead animals and plants, which sink to the bottom of the lake and form a sludge. It is grazed upon by insect larvae. The phytoplankton are eaten by tiny animals, the zooplankton, and by larger plant-feeders such as sticklebacks and carp. These are prey for meat-eaters such as pike and perch. The predatory fish may, in turn, become prey for fish-eating birds and mammals, such as herons, ospreys, mink and otters.

Carp feed on insect larvae and small plants.

A pike making a meal of a stickleback.

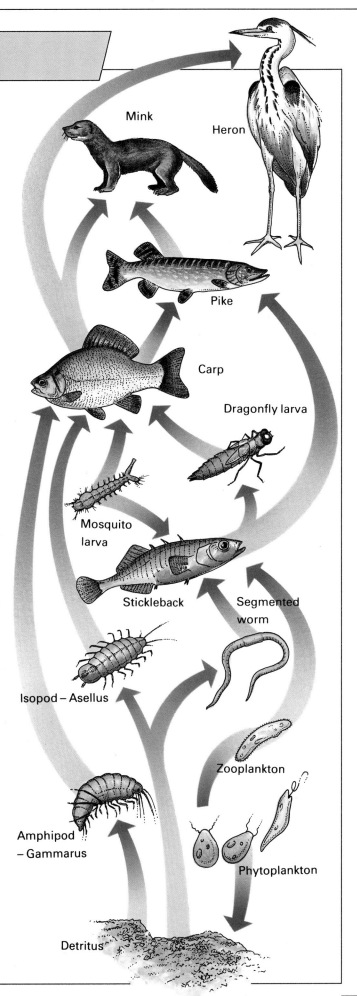

BONY FISH (Rivers and estuaries)

Major groups:
Salmon and pike (180 species), catfish (2,000), bichir and sturgeon (25), gars (7), eels (300), perch and allies (1,000), lampreys (30), mudskippers (30).

Unusual species:
Burbot, a freshwater type of cod, produces more than 1 million eggs.
Cave characin, of South America, is completely blind.

The strength of the current in a stretch of river determines the wildlife that can live there. In fast-flowing streams the only fish are strong swimmers, such as salmon and trout, or those that have suckers and can cling to rocks (for example, the sucker fish of Southeast Asia). Downstream live fish that feed on the plants, larvae and worms in silt on the riverbed. Where the current is weak, aquatic vegetation is usually rich. Here live deep-bodied fish that can weave between plants. The vegetation also provides cover for meat-eating fish that pounce on prey as it swims past. In estuaries at high tide, some sea fish swim upstream to feed in a layer of denser sea water near the bottom.

Life cycle – Atlantic salmon

Several species of fish spend their adult lives at sea but return to fresh water to breed. Among these are the salmon, ayu, and sea lamprey. Other fish live as adults in rivers and swim to the sea to breed. Famous among these are European and American eels.

Adult Atlantic salmon breed in the same river or stream where they were hatched, which they find using their sensitive sense of smell. The female lays thousands of eggs, but many are eaten by eels or birds.

The young spend one to three years in fresh water, changing from alevins, to fry, and to parr. The parr then change to smolts, which migrate to the sea. Here they spend several years. When mature, they migrate back unerringly to the place where they were born, leaping up waterfalls on the way. Then, in the shallow headwaters, they mate and lay their eggs in the gravel, to hatch the following spring. Most then die.

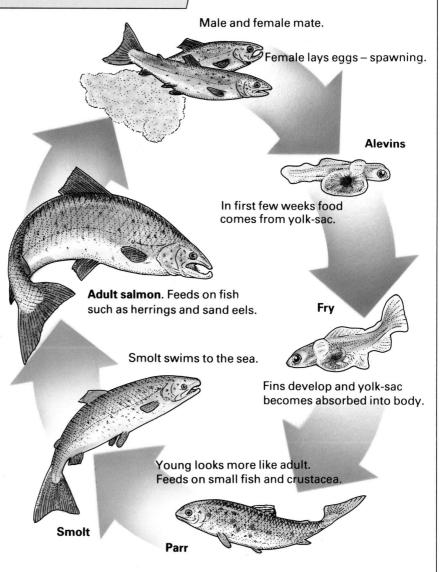

Male and female mate.

Female lays eggs – spawning.

Alevins

In first few weeks food comes from yolk-sac.

Fry

Fins develop and yolk-sac becomes absorbed into body.

Adult salmon. Feeds on fish such as herrings and sand eels.

Smolt swims to the sea.

Young looks more like adult. Feeds on small fish and crustacea.

Smolt

Parr

Out onto land

Some freshwater fish can breathe both in air and in water, and may travel across land. In autumn, when the ground is wet, adult eels migrate between rivers. They breathe through their skin, which is supplied with fine blood vessels, like a frog's skin. They also breathe aerated water carried in their gill chambers. Adult European eels migrate thousands of miles into the mid-Atlantic to breed.

An eel photographed at night while migrating over land.

Mudskippers of Indonesia can survive on land between the tides.

Mudskippers live in mangrove swamps. They have front fins that look like short stumpy arms, which they use with their tails to skip across the mud to catch insects or to climb up the banks when the tide comes in. Before coming on land, they fill their gill chambers with water and breathe in the usual way using their gills.

Feeding

Rivers and estuaries provide fish with food such as plants and worms. Fish therefore have a variety of feeding habits – surface-feeding, stirring up creatures from the riverbed, and lurking in ambush among the plants.

Sturgeon have a small mouth to suck in snails, worms and small fish. Barbels and catfish have whisker-like sense organs around their mouth which they use to detect food. Pike have rows of sharp teeth which they use to seize other fish or even small mammals and birds at the water's edge or swimming on the surface.

The Atlantic sturgeon feeds near the riverbed.

BONY FISH(Inshore waters)

Some 15,000 species, including:
herring and anchovy (350 species); anglers and frogfish (250); cod, haddock (450); John Dory (35); scorpionfish and gurnards (1,200); mackerel, tuna and remora (6,000); flatfish (550); pufferfish (350).

The animal community of seas and oceans is supported by the phytoplankton and the seaweeds and plants that grow in coastal, or inshore, waters. Most inshore fish are those with bony skeletons. There are small herring, whiting and anchovy, which swim as shoals and that people catch for food. They rely on the safety of the shoal and on their speed and drab colors to avoid the predatory cod and tuna. Flatfish, such as plaice, have both eyes on one side of the body, which can change color to blend with a sandy or muddy sea bed and give camouflage. Scorpionfish have rows of poisonous spines, and pufferfish can inflate their bodies – adaptations that make them difficult for other fish to eat.

Shoals

Striped angel fish swim in shoals for safety.

Thousands of inshore fish, among them whiting, herring and mackerel, move and feed as a large group known as a school or shoal. They swim side by side in the same direction, turning regularly in perfect harmony. Shoal fish use their lateral line system to detect currents in the water made by their neighbors and so keep a constant distance from each other. Living and moving in a shoal gives protection by reducing the chances of a predator catching any one of them. The shoal is no defense against human fishermen, however, who sometimes scoop up a whole shoal in their nets. Around coral reefs some shoal fish are brightly colored with spots and stripes that camouflage them against the dappled sunlight reflected from the coral.

Buoyancy

Unlike cartilaginous fish, which are denser than water and tend to sink unless they keep swimming, bony fish have a swim bladder, a gas-filled sac linked to or lying close above the intestines. It maintains the buoyancy of the fish to keep it suspended in the water. The sac is filled with air taken in through the mouth, or with nitrogen and oxygen passed from the blood system. Gas is let out of the sac through a valve opening to the water, or is returned to the blood. Some predatory fish use their buoyancy to remain stationary in the water, waiting for prey to swim past.

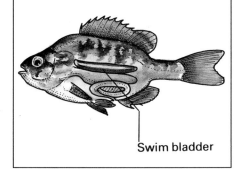

Swim bladder

Reproduction

Most sea fish produce eggs containing air sacs or oil drops, so that they float near the surface of the water. This ensures that when the young hatch they are well supplied with planktonic food. Most females lay thousands of eggs (a cod lays up to 6 million), for there is only safety in numbers. Many of the eggs are eaten by plankton-feeding fish and invertebrates, or are carried by currents to waters that are too warm or too cold for them to survive. Female seahorses, though, lay their eggs in the male's protective belly pouch. The young hatch and then stay in the pouch until they are fully developed, and when still small may swim back into the pouch for safety when danger threatens.

A male seahorse with eggs in its belly pouch

How fish swim

In swimming, a bony fish uses muscles along its body to produce a side-to-side movement of its backbone. With the help of its fins and tail, it pushes backwards and sideways against the water, steers, and stops itself dipping and rising. Using the fins on its back and underside, it steers a fairly straight course and avoids wobbling from side to side or up and down.

Flying fish can leap out of the water and glide for several meters by spreading their wing-like front paired fins. Eels, with long fins above and below, move rather like a snake.

Four-winged flying fish leap out of the waters of the Red Sea.

 Thrust of tail   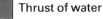 Thrust of water

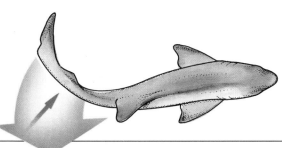

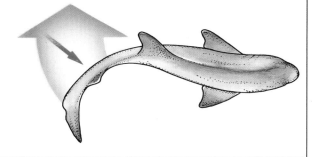

BONY FISH (Deep water)

About 2,500 species, including: spiny eels (20 species); lantern fish (300); angler fish (150); ribbon fish (50).
Longest: oarfish – up to 15m (49 ft).
Smallest: hatchet fish – 2cm (0.8 in).
Deepest living: Brotulid fish – 10,900m (36,000 ft).

In many places, oceans reach a depth of more than 10km (6 miles). But even at 1km (0.6 miles), there is no light and therefore no plants. The only food available is the rain of dead organisms from above, together with the fish and invertebrates that feed on this detritus. Yet many bony fish live there. Most are small and darkly colored. Some, such as gulper eels, have a huge mouth which they keep open at all times to catch food. Most of those that feed on the ocean floor have a downward-pointing mouth and long snout. Some have luminous organs, to attract mates or lure prey. Most remain in the ocean depths, although the 15m (49-foot) eel-like oarfish sometimes rises to the surface.

Light organs

Many free-swimming deep-sea fish possess a light organ. This is a specialized part of the body, usually near the head, or the underside, that glows in the dark. Its luminous glare is used to attract prey but may also serve to deter predators or help adult males and females of a species find each other to breed. Deep sea angler fish, which live at depths of 1,000 to 3,500m (3,300 – 11,500 ft), use their light organ as a bait to tempt inquisitive smaller fish to within reach of their huge jaws.

The light organ of a deep-sea fish glows in the dark.

Feeding

Lantern fish are deep-sea inhabitants, spending the day at depths of more than 1,000m (3,300 ft). However, at night they swim towards the surface to feed on planktonic animals. The lantern fish are in turn the food of species such as viper fish and black swallowers, which have vicious pointed teeth and expandable stomachs that allow them to gulp down fish twice their size. But with food being so scarce, even a small meal may have to last them several days.

An angler fish has a luminous lure on its head.

Fish chart

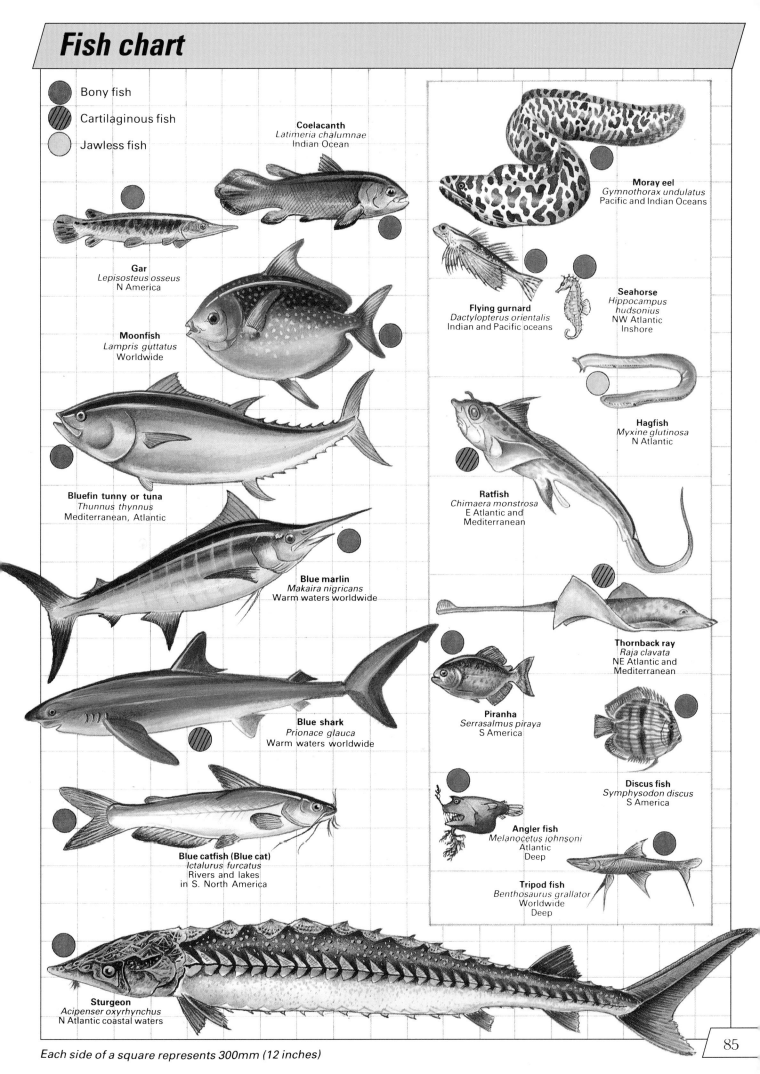

- Bony fish
- Cartilaginous fish
- Jawless fish

Coelacanth
Latimeria chalumnae
Indian Ocean

Gar
Lepisosteus osseus
N America

Moonfish
Lampris guttatus
Worldwide

Bluefin tunny or tuna
Thunnus thynnus
Mediterranean, Atlantic

Blue marlin
Makaira nigricans
Warm waters worldwide

Blue shark
Prionace glauca
Warm waters worldwide

Blue catfish (Blue cat)
Ictalurus furcatus
Rivers and lakes
in S. North America

Sturgeon
Acipenser oxyrhynchus
N Atlantic coastal waters

Moray eel
Gymnothorax undulatus
Pacific and Indian Oceans

Flying gurnard
Dactylopterus orientalis
Indian and Pacific oceans

Seahorse
*Hippocampus
hudsonius*
NW Atlantic
Inshore

Hagfish
Myxine glutinosa
N Atlantic

Ratfish
Chimaera monstrosa
E Atlantic and
Mediterranean

Thornback ray
Raja clavata
NE Atlantic and
Mediterranean

Piranha
Serrasalmus piraya
S America

Discus fish
Symphysodon discus
S America

Angler fish
Melanocetus johnsoni
Atlantic
Deep

Tripod fish
Benthosaurus grallator
Worldwide
Deep

Each side of a square represents 300mm (12 inches)

AMPHIBIANS

Major groups: earthworm-like caecilians (150 species), newts and salamanders (350), eel-like sirens and species with minute limbs (4), frogs and toads (2,700).
Distribution: all wetlands except in polar regions.
Largest: Japanese and Chinese giant salamanders – 1.8m (6ft) long, 65kg (143lb) in weight.
Smallest: Arrow-poison frog – 8.5mm (0.3 in) long.

The name amphibian comes from two Greek words – *amphi* meaning both, and *bios* life. Young amphibians live in water. Like fish, they breathe using gills, use a tail and fins for swimming, and have a lateral line system. Adult amphibians are adapted mainly for life on land. They breathe using lungs or through their skin, have two pairs of limbs for walking or jumping, and have eyes, ears and a nose like those of true land vertebrates. Yet few adult amphibians are entirely independent of water. Most breed in water because their eggs need moisture, and amphibians dry out if their skin cannot be kept moist. Some American tree frogs, for example, spend their entire lives in trees, using rainwater "puddles" that collect at the bases of leaves to keep moist and for laying their eggs.

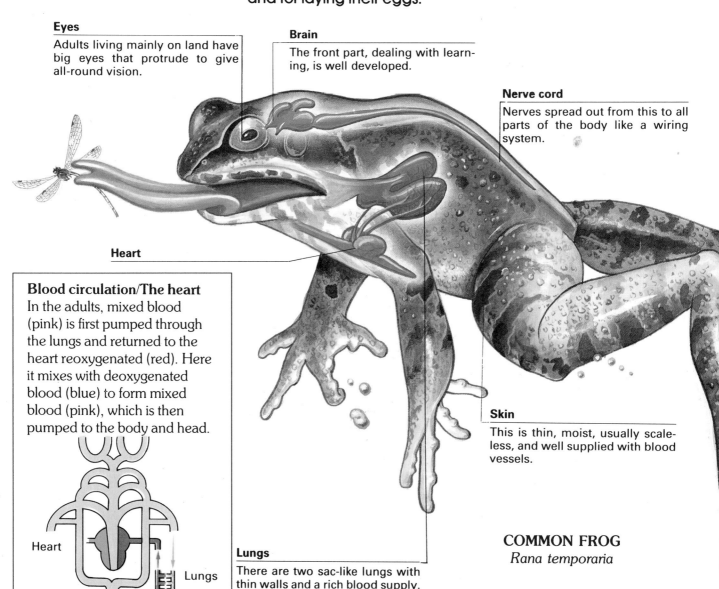

Eyes
Adults living mainly on land have big eyes that protrude to give all-round vision.

Brain
The front part, dealing with learning, is well developed.

Nerve cord
Nerves spread out from this to all parts of the body like a wiring system.

Heart

Blood circulation/The heart
In the adults, mixed blood (pink) is first pumped through the lungs and returned to the heart reoxygenated (red). Here it mixes with deoxygenated blood (blue) to form mixed blood (pink), which is then pumped to the body and head.

Heart

Lungs

Skin
This is thin, moist, usually scaleless, and well supplied with blood vessels.

Lungs
There are two sac-like lungs with thin walls and a rich blood supply.

COMMON FROG
Rana temporaria

Metamorphosis

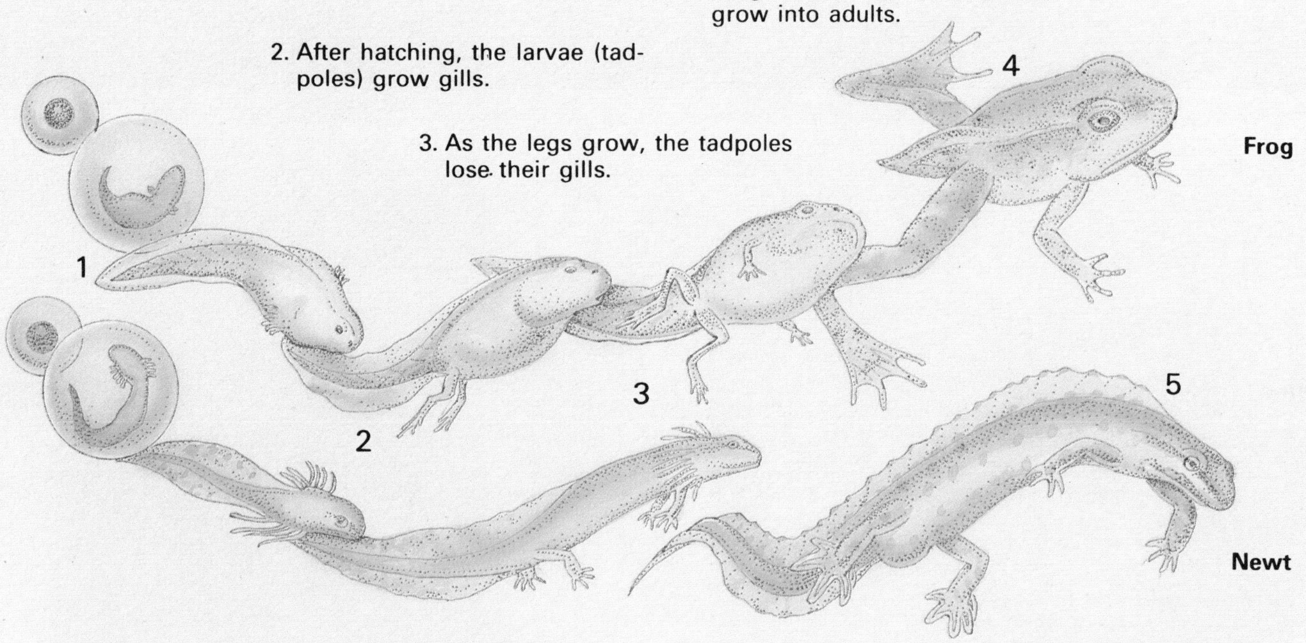

1. Female frogs and newts lay egg masses called spawn.

2. After hatching, the larvae (tadpoles) grow gills.

3. As the legs grow, the tadpoles lose their gills.

4. Frogs lose their tail as they grow into adults.

5. Newts keep their tails and some species grow a frill along the back.

1

2

3

4

5

Frog

Newt

A common feature of most amphibians, and certainly of the familiar frogs and toads, is that they undergo a complete change in appearance and internal body structure during their life history. The gradual change from aquatic larva to land-living adult is known as metamorphosis. In newts and salamanders this change is less dramatic.

The adult amphibians breed in water. The female produces eggs (spawn) that are protected by a layer of jelly. After a few days to several weeks the larvae, or tadpoles, hatch. Those of frogs and toads feed on tiny water plants, whereas newt larvae eat insect larvae and small soft-shelled animals. Then, the tadpoles start to take on adult features. They begin to lose their gills, and as their lungs grow they come to the surface to breathe. They start to eat insects such as flies and worms. Legs begin to grow – first the back ones and then the front ones – and the tail gets shorter and shorter (in frogs and toads) until it disappears. The young adults are then ready to come out on land.

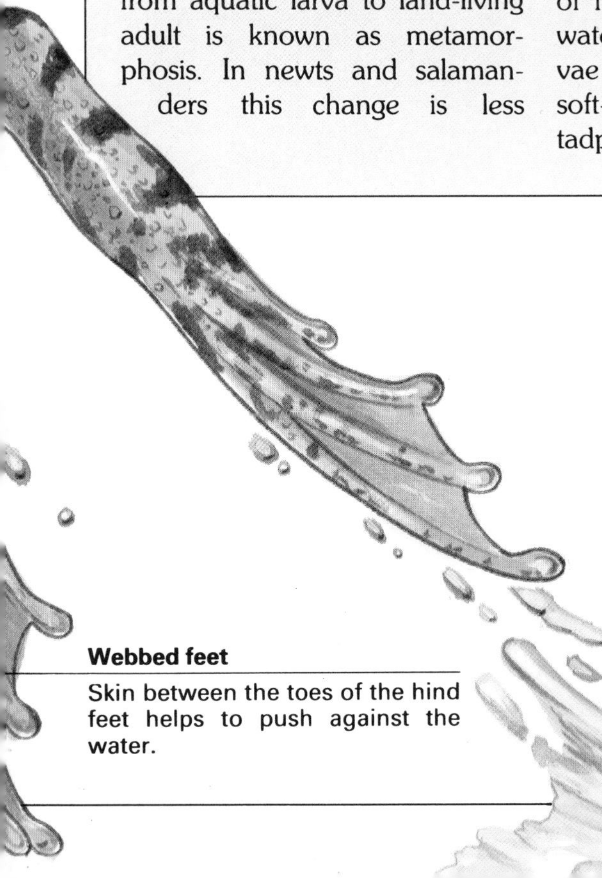

Skeleton

Except for lack of ribs, this is like the skeleton of true land vertebrates.

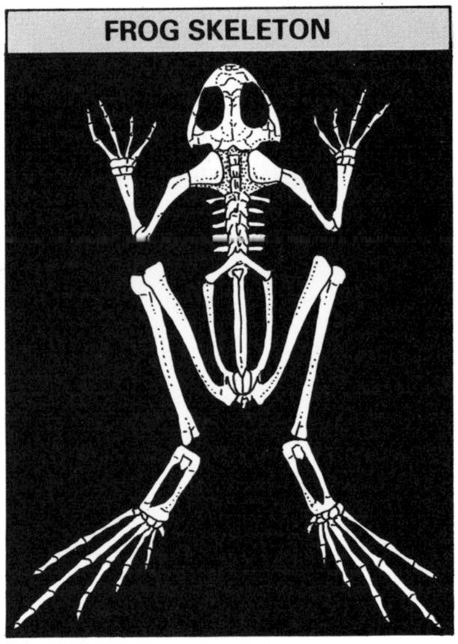

Webbed feet

Skin between the toes of the hind feet helps to push against the water.

FROG SKELETON

Living on land

Frogs and toads have powerful muscles in their hind legs, which they use to jump from place to place, although some toads generally crawl. Some species have adhesive pads and hand-like front feet that allow them to climb. Newts and salamanders raise their bodies off the ground and walk on all fours when they are on land. Limbless caecilians move like earth-worms. Sirens and amphiuma have minute legs, are mostly aquatic and swim like eels.

The fire salamander walks like a lizard.

Feeding

All adult amphibians are carnivorous. They have large mouths that can hold prey intact and still alive. Their jaws are strong, and in most newts and salamanders, bear upper and lower sets of teeth. Many species have tongues that can shoot out to capture prey. The diet of amphibians includes spiders, insects, worms, fish, reptiles, and mice and other small mammals. Some toads have a poisonous slime on their skin, which stops them from being eaten.

The Alpine newt feeds mainly on worms.

Breeding

The adults cannot breed until they are a few years old. At mating time, male newts and salamanders often acquire bright and showy colors, crests and tail membranes. These are used in courtship displays. Most male frogs and toads attract females using their voice – their croaks are mating calls. Mating takes place in the water. Often large numbers of adults group together in ponds to breed. In some species, the male produces a mass of sperm which the female takes up into her body to fertilize her eggs. In others, the female sheds the eggs into the water and the male sprays them with sperm. Females produce from a few dozen to 30,000 eggs. Many eggs are eaten by fish and other amphibia or are killed by adverse weather, so few hatch into tadpoles. Tadpoles are also a favorite prey of aquatic predators and many more are killed before maturing into adults.

Mating toads and chains of black-egged spawn

Growth

Throughout its life, the Mexican salamander, or axolotl, usually retains its gills and remains in water. Until the mid-19th century, it was believed to be a unique type of amphibian that never experienced metamorphosis. But although the axolotl looks like a larval amphibian, it can, like an adult, mate and produce offspring. It simply lacks a certain chemical, a growth hormone, that is essential for metamorphosis. If the hormone is added to the pond water in which it lives, or if the pond dries up, the axolotl loses it gills and changes to a typical adult land-living salamander. It returns to water only at mating time to lay its eggs. Cave salamanders, which live for up to sixty years, spend all their time in complete darkness.

The axolotl can reproduce even at the larval stage.

Amphibians chart

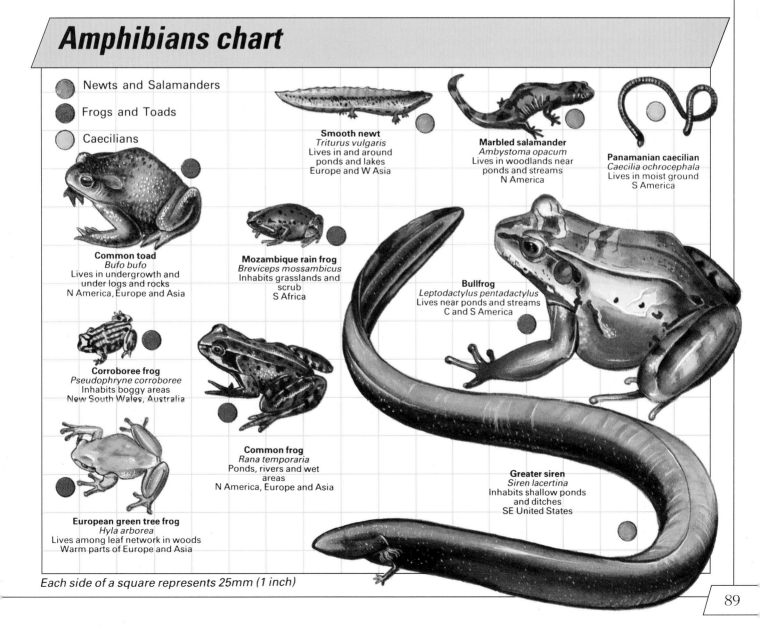

- Newts and Salamanders
- Frogs and Toads
- Caecilians

Smooth newt
Triturus vulgaris
Lives in and around ponds and lakes
Europe and W Asia

Marbled salamander
Ambystoma opacum
Lives in woodlands near ponds and streams
N America

Panamanian caecilian
Caecilia ochrocephala
Lives in moist ground
S America

Common toad
Bufo bufo
Lives in undergrowth and under logs and rocks
N America, Europe and Asia

Mozambique rain frog
Breviceps mossambicus
Inhabits grasslands and scrub
S Africa

Bullfrog
Leptodactylus pentadactylus
Lives near ponds and streams
C and S America

Corroboree frog
Pseudophryne corroboree
Inhabits boggy areas
New South Wales, Australia

Common frog
Rana temporaria
Ponds, rivers and wet areas
N America, Europe and Asia

Greater siren
Siren lacertina
Inhabits shallow ponds and ditches
SE United States

European green tree frog
Hyla arborea
Lives among leaf network in woods
Warm parts of Europe and Asia

Each side of a square represents 25mm (1 inch)

REPTILES

Major groups: turtles and tortoises (250 species), lizards and snakes (6,000), crocodiles and alligators (25). Extinct groups include dinosaurs.
Distribution: worldwide except polar regions.
Largest: Estuarine crocodile of Australasia, southeastern Asia – weight 2 tons, length 8.6m (28.3 ft).
Smallest: A gecko, found only in the British Virgin Islands – 18mm (0.7in).

Reptiles are the most advanced of all cold-blooded vertebrates. They are adapted best to living on land, although many species, such as turtles and crocodiles, spend most of the time in water. Reptiles breathe air using lungs, have a thick leathery skin that stops their body from drying up in hot weather, and most lay eggs that have a hard shell or tough leathery skin to protect the embryo. Unlike amphibians, reptiles do not have an aquatic larval stage. The newborn are miniature versions of the adults. Reptiles evolved from early amphibians about 300 million years ago. Some, like the dinosaurs, grew to enormous sizes. Others were ancestors of birds and mammals.

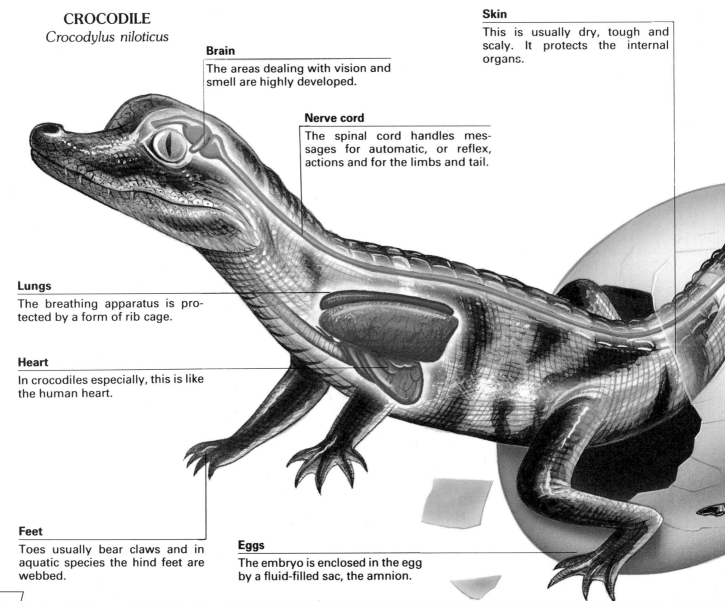

CROCODILE
Crocodylus niloticus

Brain
The areas dealing with vision and smell are highly developed.

Nerve cord
The spinal cord handles messages for automatic, or reflex, actions and for the limbs and tail.

Skin
This is usually dry, tough and scaly. It protects the internal organs.

Lungs
The breathing apparatus is protected by a form of rib cage.

Heart
In crocodiles especially, this is like the human heart.

Feet
Toes usually bear claws and in aquatic species the hind feet are webbed.

Eggs
The embryo is enclosed in the egg by a fluid-filled sac, the amnion.

Blood circulation/The heart

The heart has three main chambers. The left atrium collects deoxygenated blood (blue) from the body. This is pumped by the ventricle through the lungs and returns via the right atrium. The ventricle then pumps this oxygenated blood (red) through to the head and body.

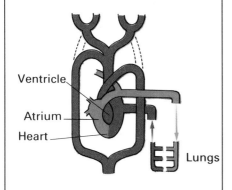

Ventricle
Atrium
Heart
Lungs

Skeleton

There are three regions: the skull and neck, backbone and limbs, and tail.

Cold-blooded

Lizard warms up in early sunlight.

As the Sun goes down, it emerges to be active again.

In the midday heat, it rests in shade.

When the weather turns cold, reptiles become sleepy and unable to move about with their usual speed as their heartbeat and rate of breathing slow down. When it is very hot, they must shelter from the Sun's rays. This is because they are cold-blooded, which means they have no internal mechanism to regulate their body temperature. Their blood acquires the temperature of their surroundings. Reptiles are generally most active at a blood temperature in the narrow range of 30-35°C (86-97°F). They tend to alternate bouts of great activity with long periods of rest. When active, or as they bask in the Sun, their temperature rises. As it increases well above normal, they rest in shade, slink into water, or burrow into the ground. Blood temperature then falls. For this reason, most reptiles live in warm climates, but even there few of them are active at night when it is cool unless, like crocodiles, they hunt in the water.

SKELETON OF A CROCODILE (*Crocodylus niloticus*)

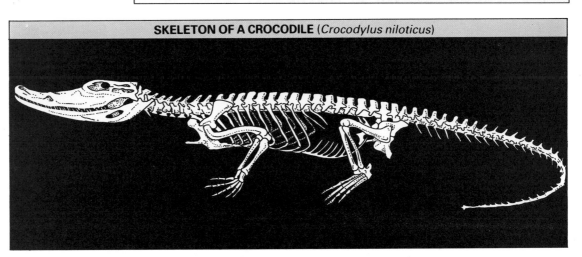

CROCODILES AND ALLIGATORS

The crocodile family includes true crocodiles (about 15 species: common in Africa, S. America, S. Asia, Australasia), alligators and caiman (9 species: N. and S. America, China), gharial or gavial (1 species: India, Bangladesh and Pakistan).
Lifespan: 40+ years.

The closest living relatives of dinosaurs and the largest of living reptiles are members of the crocodile family (alligators and crocodiles). They have evolved for life in water and inhabit swamps and rivers in warm areas of the world. They have powerful jaws lined with sharp teeth, and once the jaws close on a prey it never escapes. All have a heavy body and an armor of bony scales. The tail is long and flattened like a paddle. Used with a whip-like action, it allows efficient swimming. On land, crocodiles are generally slow movers but can run fast. They slither along on their stomachs or raise their bodies off the ground and waddle. Crocodiles lay white eggs in the ground.

Feeding

Crocodiles are meat-eaters. They hunt mainly small land animals and fish. Once the prey is caught, it is dragged into the water, drowned, then eaten straight away or left to rot before being eaten. Gharials eat only fish. Some crocodiles will attack humans. All crocodiles have pointed teeth designed for catching and holding prey. The main differences between members of the family are the number of teeth, length and width of head, and in true crocodiles the fourth lower tooth is visible when the mouth is closed. In alligators and caimans the upper teeth are more prominent.

An American alligator attacks a young egret.

Alligator

Caiman

Crocodile

Gharial

Breathing

Living in water requires special adaptations for breathing air. Crocodiles have eyes, ears and nostrils on top of their head and snout so that they can see, hear and breathe when almost completely submerged. When under water, the windpipe, ears and nostrils can be closed with special flaps so that the mouth can be kept open to feed. The animals swim with eyelids open, but under water the eyes are covered by a transparent membrane so that the animals can still see their prey. Other aquatic reptiles, like turtles, can absorb oxygen from water taken into their body, and stay submerged for several hours at a time. They always return to the surface to breathe.

A submerged crocodile with only its eyes and nostrils showing.

Growth

Mother crocodiles lay up to 50 eggs and guard their nest until the young hatch out but do not usually care for the newborn, although they may carry the baby crocodiles carefully in their jaws and put them in a safe place. Many of the emerging crocodiles fall prey to birds, mammals and other reptiles. The newborn are miniature adults. They can immediately walk, swim and catch their own food. They grow rapidly at first. Some alligators increase in length by 30cm (12in) a year for the first few years of their life, growing eventually to a length of 5m (16 feet) or more. Most crocodiles and alligators reach sexual maturity when about eight years old.

A young alligator is safe sitting on its mother's head.

LIZARDS

Major types: Geckos (700 species), iguanas (630), agamids (300), chameleons (90), skinks (600), African and Eurasian lizards (150), South American lizards (200), slow-worms (75), worm lizards (120), monitors (25). Related to and resembling lizards is the tuatara of New Zealand, which has a strange third eye on top of its head.

Ranging from the aggressive 3m (10ft) long Komodo dragon of Indonesia to the small harmless green lizards and wall lizards familiar in temperate areas, these reptiles are highly successful. They have adapted to many different lifestyles. The North American Gila monsters and beaded lizards have a poisonous bite and prey on small rodents. Worm lizards, slow-worms and some skinks have no limbs. They may burrow underground to feed on earthworms and slugs. Geckos are mostly nocturnal and climb trees to prey on insects. Flying dragons have a membrane of skin between their toes, which they spread out so that they can glide between the trees in which they live.

Self-defense

The green coloration common in tree-living lizards and the patchy colors of lizards that scurry around in dry grass or climb over walls act as camouflage. Chameleons can change their colors to merge with their surroundings, although this may be to give them a chance to attack prey rather than for self-defense. Other lizards, such as the thorny devils and girdled lizards, have weapons such as facial, body or tail spikes. They use these to warn off would-be attackers. Frilled lizards use a display of force and terror to defend themselves. They spread out a frill around their necks, open their brightly colored mouths, and in this way look much more aggressive than they really are.

Many lizards shed their tail when attacked and later grow a new one. Their enemy is fooled by the decoy. In chameleons, color changes of the skin are produced by special cells known as chromatophores. These contain granules of several colored pigments. Depending on messages received from the brain via the spinal cord, the cells are made to expand or contract in the desired way.

A frilled lizard stands and faces an attacker.

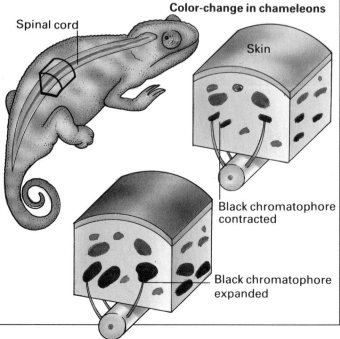

Color-change in chameleons

Spinal cord

Skin

Black chromatophore contracted

Black chromatophore expanded

Feeding

Lizards' food consists mainly of insects such as flies, ants, termites and grasshoppers. Some species supplement this diet with worms, snails, birds' eggs, small rodents and other mammals, and even fruit and other reptiles. Lizards generally swallow their prey whole. They grasp the food in their jaws then gobble it up in a series of snatching movements of the mouth. When catching insects in particular, many lizards use their tongue as a hunting weapon. Chameleons, for example, have a sticky tongue almost as long as their body and tail which they shoot out at lightning speed and with amazing accuracy to catch their prey. They then pull the tongue back into the mouth together with their meal stuck to the end. In this manner, they can sometimes successfully catch even birds. Each eye can move independently, giving them a wide field of vision and allowing them to judge distance very accurately. A prehensile tail serves as a fifth limb.

A three-horned chameleon catches a fly.

Movement

Most lizards have four legs and can walk and run. They differ from mammals in having legs that stick out on each side of the body rather than under it. They usually move slowly, bending their bodies side to side to push themselves along. Desert lizards, such as the African gridiron-tailed lizard, can run along on just two legs. They lift their heads and stomachs off the ground, rear up on their hind legs, and scurry along. Their long tails act as a counter-balance. Some lizards are adept at climbing. Limbless lizards, for example skinks, slow-worms and other burrowing species, resemble and move like snakes.

The basilisk lizard can run across a pond's surface.

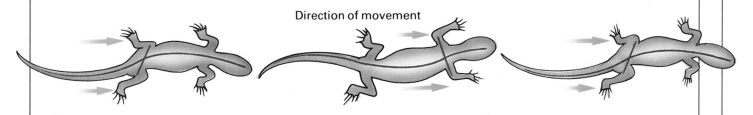

Direction of movement

Hind limbs push hard against ground   Front limbs pull body forward   Hind limbs exert force again

TORTOISES AND TURTLES

Major groups: Snapper and mud turtles (25 species), tortoises and freshwater turtles (115), leathery turtle (1), marine turtles (5), side-necked turtles (45).
Largest: Pacific leatherback turtle – 2.2m (7 ft) long, weighing 500kg (1200 lb).
Longest lived: Seychelles Marion's tortoise – 155 years.
Slowest moving: Seychelles giant tortoise – 0.37 kph (0.23 mph).

With a body surrounded by a protective shell, these are the oldest group of reptiles, and have hardly changed in 200 million years. There are three main groups. Tortoises live on land, have a domed shell, stumpy legs and feed mostly on plants. Their relatives, freshwater turtles, live in rivers and lakes. They are plant- and meat-eaters. The second group, turtles, comprises mostly marine creatures. Their shell is flatter and they have paddle-shaped feet used for swimming. The third group, side-necked turtles and their allies, live in fresh water but tuck their heads under the edge of the shell instead of pulling it in. All aquatic species come to the surface of the water to gulp air into their lungs. Also, although they may mate in the water, females of aquatic species come ashore to lay their eggs in a hollow in the ground. They then return to the water, leaving the eggs to hatch on their own.

Life cycle

Among tortoises and turtles, the breeding season begins with males approaching females. Mating may last hours, and because of the animals' shells, males often have to stand almost upright to fertilize the eggs successfully. Mother tortoises lay their eggs in a shallow depression or natural hole in the ground and leave them to hatch in the sun. Female marine turtles lay their eggs in holes dug on sandy beaches and cover them with sand. This serves to hide the eggs from predators such as sea-birds, and to keep them warm. Days or weeks later the young hatch out. They must struggle to the surface and make their way as fast as they can to the sea. Many are caught and eaten by crabs, snakes and birds. With turtles, adulthood is reached between 12-15 years, and they are among the longest-lived animals. Giant tortoises of the Galapagos Islands, for example, are known to live for more than a hundred years.

A leathery turtle scrapes a hole for its eggs.

Newly hatched leathery turtles scuttle to the sea.

Shells

The shell, or carapace, is composed of bony plates covered by horny scales. The arched upper shell is fused to the back bone and to the ribs, which thus cannot be use din breathing. Instead air is drawn into the lungs by a pumping action of muscles. The undershell is less heavily armored. Upper and lower shell are joined in the middle region on each side, leaving openings in front and behind for the head, legs and tail. In most species, the head can be withdrawn under the carapace. The shell of a tortoise grows throughout life, but growth stops during hibernation. As a result, the patterns on the shell have growth rings, which can be used to estimate the animal's age.

Shell shapes among tortoises of some Galapagos Islands

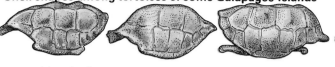

abingdoni   *elephantopus*   *galapagoensis*   *ephippium*

The giant tortoise can be identified by the shape of its shell.

Feeding

Instead of teeth, tortoises, turtles and sea turtles have a horny beak with sharp cutting edges. These beaks cannot shred or crush food. Also, their broad, fleshy tongues cannot be protruded to collect morsels of food. They are forced to seize plant or animal food in their jaws and chop it into large pieces and swallow it slowly.

A Greek tortoise feeding on lettuce leaves.

Migration

Adult marine turtles, such as the green turtle, migrate each year in great numbers from feeding areas in shallow parts of the sea to the same distant breeding ground. There they haul themselves onto land, moving clumsily up the beach, lay their eggs and bury them in the sand, then return to the sea until the next breeding season.

The green turtle swims to the shore to breed.

SNAKES

Major groups: blind snakes (275 species), burrowing shield-tailed snakes (50), constrictors (70), water snakes (2), vipers (100), cobras and sea-snakes (200), Colubrid snakes (1,500).
Longest: Reticulated python – 8.7m (28.5ft).
Most poisonous: Sea snake of N.W. Australian waters.

With their long, slender, limbless bodies, lack of eardrums, and eyelids fused to form a transparent protective covering over the eyes, present-day snakes probably evolved from lizards. Most snakes live in warm places, inhabiting deserts, tropical forests and grasslands, where they use various methods of moving along the ground. They are adapted to a life above ground, although some live in water, where they produce live young. Snakes eat live animals and the eggs of birds and other reptiles, which they usually swallow whole. They can swallow prey larger than themselves. Some species are poisonous, although most snakes are harmless to humans.

Jaws

Snakes are unique among reptiles in that they can move their upper and lower jaws apart during swallowing. Because each jaw can move independently, and with flexible elastic ligaments linking the halves of the lower jaw, snakes can open their mouth enormously wide. A large python can devour a small antelope, pig or monkey whole. To help swallow such large prey, they have evolved several features. First, they have backward pointing teeth to grip the food and pull it back into the mouth (and the front-fanged vipers and rattlesnakes can fold their fangs back out of the way when swallowing prey). Second, the whole brain is encased in bone so it cannot easily get damaged. Third, the rib cage can enlarge to allow large items to pass down the throat. Also, because snakes have no legs, they lack the bones that would form shoulder and hip girdles, which means they can consume prey wider than their bodies.

An African egg-eating snake

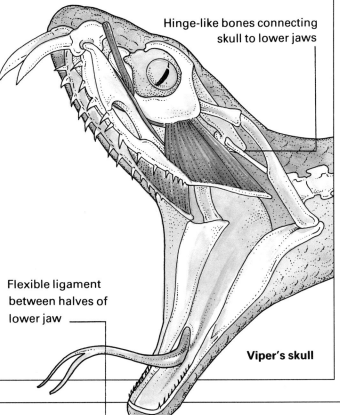

Hinge-like bones connecting skull to lower jaws

Flexible ligament between halves of lower jaw

Viper's skull

Killing and feeding

Snakes must first kill or render their prey unconscious. Boas and pythons seize the prey in their jaws, wrap themselves round it, and then stop it breathing. They are known as constrictors. Smaller snakes kill or stun their prey using venom, which is a mixture of poisons. Venom is injected through a pair of special teeth called fangs. Vipers have long front fangs that fold back when not in use. Their venom attacks the prey's blood system. Cobras have fixed short front fangs and produce a venom affecting the nervous system. Colubrids, such as the bird-eating Boomslang snake, have poisonous fangs at the back of the jaw. They attract prey by flicking out their brightly colored tongues. Grass snakes also have small fixed fangs at the back of the jaw, but do not have a bite harmful to humans.

A black-necked spitting cobra

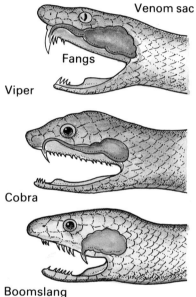

Viper

Cobra

Boomslang

A python crushes a gazelle and begins to swallow it whole.

Movement

Snakes have no legs and have evolved their own way of moving on land. A snake can use its tail as a lever to push its head and trunk forwards then, with its neck, pull the rest of its body along. In serpentine motion the snake adopts a wave-like action and pushes against objects to gain leverage. In water, snakes use this action to swim, and many sea snakes have a flattened tail which acts like an oar or paddle. On loose soil or sand, snakes arch their head forwards, put it down in a sideways loop, then draw up the rest of the body. Snakes that move in this way are called sidewinders.

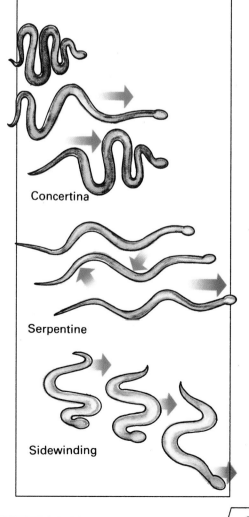

Concertina

Serpentine

Sidewinding

Mating

Male snakes often compete for or display to the females by using elaborate dances. Rival males may entwine their entire bodies in a show of strength. Males trail the females by detecting the scent of skin secretions. To mate, partners lie alongside each other, and tropical species may breed several times a year. Sea snakes usually give birth to live young but many land species lay eggs. Few tend their eggs, and the young must fend for themselves.

European adders entwined while mating

Growth

Snakes, like lizards, from time to time shed the horny layer of skin which covers their scales. This is to allow for growth. Young snakes may shed, or slough, the skin six or seven times a year. The old skin splits, usually around the lips, and the snake wriggles out, peeling it off like a glove. After sloughing the snake looks as if it has been freshly painted. A rattlesnake grows a new segment on the rattle at the end of its tail each time the skin is shed.

A Gaboon viper after shedding its skin

Senses

Vision and hearing are less highly developed than the sense of smell. Most snakes see things in only black and white, and not color. Some, especially burrowing species, are blind. Yet rattlesnakes can detect moving objects at distances of 45m (50yd). All snakes have ears that are sensitive to only low-frequency sounds. However, they seem able to detect vibrations in the ground via nerve cells around bones in the head. Their tongues are more sensitive to smell and touch. The main organ of smell, Jacobson's organ, is positioned on the roof of the animal's mouth. By flicking its tongue, a snake transfers scent particles to sensitive cells lining the organ. During swallowing, the tongue is carefully kept flat on the floor of the mouth so that it does not get injured. Some snakes, called pit vipers, can sense the body heat of warm-blooded prey such as rats, squirrels and birds using temperature sensitive pits next to their eyes. These heat-sensors work even in complete darkness.

A large-headed tree snake from Costa Rica

Reptiles chart

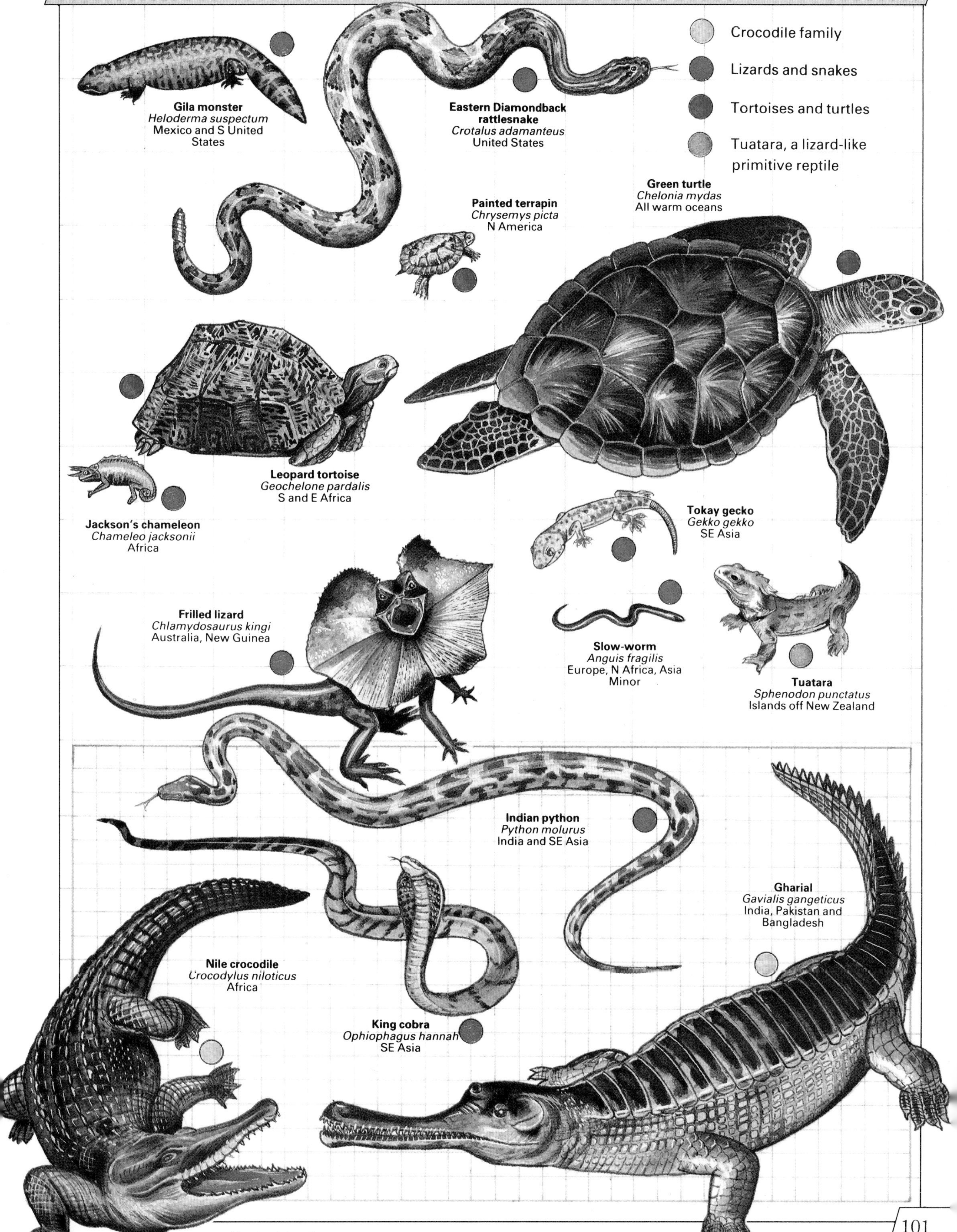

Crocodile family

Lizards and snakes

Tortoises and turtles

Tuatara, a lizard-like primitive reptile

Gila monster
Heloderma suspectum
Mexico and S United States

Eastern Diamondback rattlesnake
Crotalus adamanteus
United States

Painted terrapin
Chrysemys picta
N America

Green turtle
Chelonia mydas
All warm oceans

Leopard tortoise
Geochelone pardalis
S and E Africa

Jackson's chameleon
Chameleo jacksonii
Africa

Tokay gecko
Gekko gekko
SE Asia

Frilled lizard
Chlamydosaurus kingi
Australia, New Guinea

Slow-worm
Anguis fragilis
Europe, N Africa, Asia Minor

Tuatara
Sphenodon punctatus
Islands off New Zealand

Indian python
Python molurus
India and SE Asia

Gharial
Gavialis gangeticus
India, Pakistan and Bangladesh

Nile crocodile
Crocodylus niloticus
Africa

King cobra
Ophiophagus hannah
SE Asia

Each side of a square represents 150mm (6 inches)

BIRDS & MAMMALS

CONTENTS

INTRODUCTION

Birds were the first warm-blooded animals to take
to the air. They have evolved into a wide variety
of forms to take advantage of all habitats on Earth,
and all kinds of food. Some specialize in eating
plant foods – fruit, nuts, seeds and even honey and
nectar. Others have a diet consisting entirely of
insects. And yet others are efficient hunters, feeding on
other animals, including snakes and fish. From the Arctic
to the tropics, on land and in the water, every region of
the world has its bird life. But all share the common feature
of laying eggs.

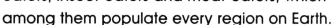

Apart from one or two primitive species, all mammals give
birth to live young, which initially feed on mother's milk. They
share a basic four-legged body plan, although in some –
such as seals and whales – the limbs have become flippers
for swimming and they share their habitats with fish. In
bats, the front limbs have evolved as wings so
that they can fly and compete with birds. Mammals
are insulated with fur or fat so they can live and be active
in all climates. And as with birds, mammals include plant-
eaters, insect-eaters and meat-eaters, which
among them populate every region on Earth.

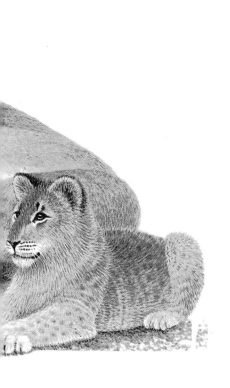

BIRDS

There are 27 groups of birds.
Biggest group: Passerines, the perching birds. This includes familiar types such as crows and sparrows (5,150 species).
Smallest group: Struthioniformes, with just one species, the ostrich.
Most common species: African quelea finch – more than 100 billion.
Rarest species: California condor – fewer than 10 in the wild.

There are about 8,500 different species or kinds of birds, making them the most numerous backboned animals living on land. They range in size from tiny hummingbirds only 5.5cm (2.2in) long to the ostrich, which may be more than 2.2m (7ft) tall. They are found on every continent and in all habitats from tropical forest and desert to arctic tundra and ice. But they all have in common the fact that they are warm-blooded – that is, they can keep their bodies at a constant temperature, usually about 40°C (104°F). The front limbs – legs in most reptiles and mammals – have become modified as wings, usually used for flight, and feathers provide the main body covering, with scales on the legs and toes. Feathers trap heat under them and provide large surfaces needed for flight. Birds have no teeth, but have lightweight beaks (made of horn) covering the jaws.

Flight

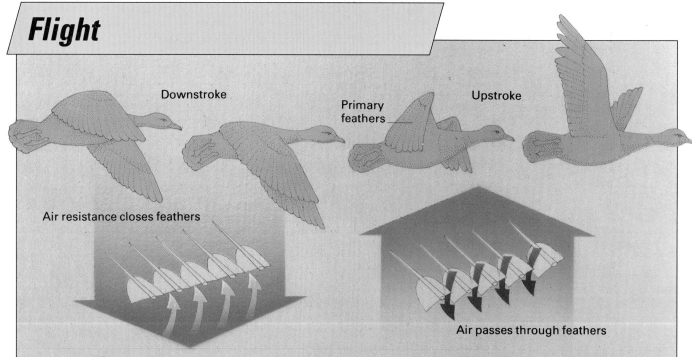

Downstroke

Primary feathers

Upstroke

Air resistance closes feathers

Air passes through feathers

The streamlined shape of a bird helps it slip easily through the air as it flies, driven through the air by its wings acting as propellers. The power to work the wings comes from large muscles on the bird's chest on each side of the breastbone. Tendons run from these to the wing bones. There is little muscle in the wings themselves, which are light and easy to swing. The inner part of the wings helps give the bird lift as it moves forward. It acts rather like the wing of an airplane. The outer part of the wings, with its long primary feathers, gives the forward push, with the primaries bending so that they help the animal forward on the upstroke as well as the downstroke. As the bird makes a downstroke the feathers are flattened against the air, making an airtight surface. On the upstroke they are turned so that air can spill between them. Flying actions and the wing shapes are adapted to the animals' needs and the type of country they inhabit.

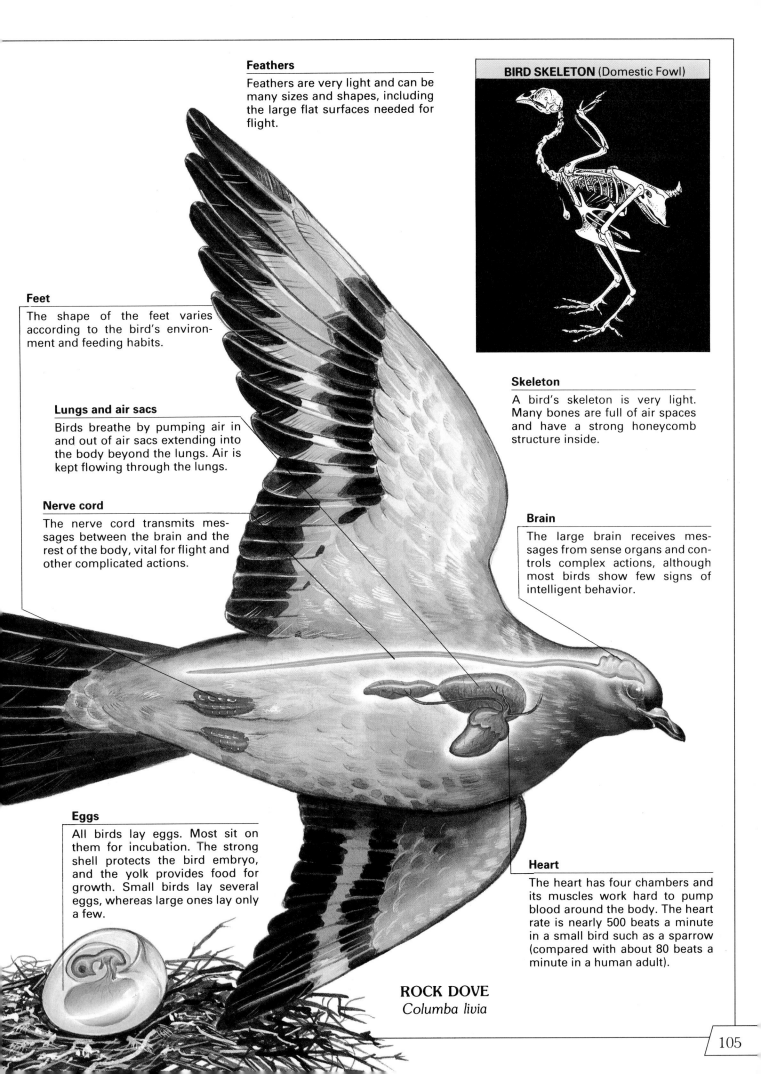

Feathers

Feathers are very light and can be many sizes and shapes, including the large flat surfaces needed for flight.

Feet

The shape of the feet varies according to the bird's environment and feeding habits.

Lungs and air sacs

Birds breathe by pumping air in and out of air sacs extending into the body beyond the lungs. Air is kept flowing through the lungs.

Nerve cord

The nerve cord transmits messages between the brain and the rest of the body, vital for flight and other complicated actions.

Skeleton

A bird's skeleton is very light. Many bones are full of air spaces and have a strong honeycomb structure inside.

Brain

The large brain receives messages from sense organs and controls complex actions, although most birds show few signs of intelligent behavior.

Eggs

All birds lay eggs. Most sit on them for incubation. The strong shell protects the bird embryo, and the yolk provides food for growth. Small birds lay several eggs, whereas large ones lay only a few.

Heart

The heart has four chambers and its muscles work hard to pump blood around the body. The heart rate is nearly 500 beats a minute in a small bird such as a sparrow (compared with about 80 beats a minute in a human adult).

ROCK DOVE
Columba livia

105

SEED- AND INSECT-EATERS

Major types: Seed-eaters include pigeons, parrots and specialist feeders such as finches. Other birds, ranging from ostriches to pheasants, take seeds as part of their diet. Insect-eaters include specialist types such as swifts, bee-eaters and treecreepers. Plant-eating birds often feed their young on insects.

Seeds and insects are two of the most abundant sources of food for birds, and there are more birds specialized for these diets than for any other. Insects are caught in the air by swallows and nightjars, picked from the surface of leaves and twigs by warblers, dug out from bark by woodpeckers, or scratched from the soil. Seeds can also be gathered in many ways, but they are harder to digest. Seed-eating birds have strong muscular gizzards, or grinding-stomachs, in which seeds are ground by the grit swallowed with the food. The first part of the gut, the crop, stores food after it is swallowed. The food is ground by the grit in the gizzard and digested.

Beaks and food

Some birds have all-purpose beaks and feed on many foods. Specialists feed on just one type of food and usually have a beak that is fully adapted to make the best job of the vital task of feeding. Many seed-eaters have a short conical beak, good for picking and cracking seeds. But there are variations depending on which seeds they eat most. Among finches, the bullfinch has a large powerful bill; it feeds on seeds, buds and shoots. The redpoll uses its smaller narrower bill like tweezers for picking the small seeds of birch and other trees. The oddly shaped beak of the crossbill can extract seeds from the cones of firs and pines.

Insect-eaters tend to have rather thin pointed beaks which they use like forceps to pick at their small prey, but again there are many variations according to the insect prey and the catching method used. Birds such as swifts that chase insects in the air have a huge gape to act as an aerial fishing net. The treecreeper has a thin beak that can be pushed deep into bark crevices. The long, strong beak of a woodpecker can drill a hole in bark so the long tongue can be used to probe for insects underneath. The Hawaiian akiapolaau also probes bark for insects with its long beak, whereas the Maui parrotbill tears into bark with its powerful beak to reach beetles.

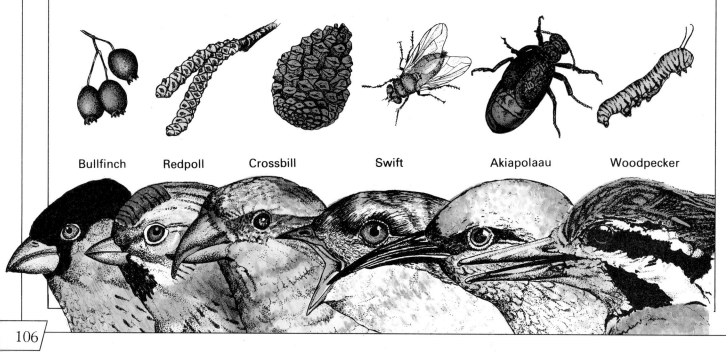

Bullfinch   Redpoll   Crossbill   Swift   Akiapolaau   Woodpecker

Care of plumage

A bird must keep its feathers in good condition if they are to function properly. A small bird may have as many as 3,000 feathers, a big bird more than 20,000. Birds molt or shed old feathers, with new ones growing below at regular intervals. The feathers are lost in a regular sequence, a few at a time, equally balanced on each side of the body. They are kept in condition by frequent preening, when the bird uses its beak and claws to tidy and comb them. It smears the feathers with a thin layer of waterproofing oil from a preen gland at the base of the tail. Many birds take baths in shallow pools, dipping and shaking their plumage. These actions discourage parasites such as mites and lice.

A small bird washing its feathers

Nests

The chicks of most small seed-eaters and insect-eaters are hatched naked and helpless, and are fed by their parents for many days before they are able to look after themselves. As adults, these birds build nests in which to lay their eggs and rear their families. Some, like chickadees, nest in tree holes, lining the cavity. Many make cup nests in trees and bushes, using a variety of materials. The reed warbler, for example, weaves a nest of grass. The most elaborately woven nests are those of weaver birds, which often make their ball nests in colonies. Many martins make cup nests and South American ovenbirds make large enclosed nests using plastered mud and blades of grass.

A woodpecker makes a hole in a tree for a nest.

Reed warbler

Weaver bird

Ovenbird

Sand martin

Swallows make nests of mud and straw.

BIRDS OF PREY

Diurnal or daytime types:
Order Falconiformes – about 280 species, including falcons, eagles, hawks and vultures. **Largest:** Andean condor – 1.15m (3.7ft) long. **Smallest:** Pygmy falcon – 14cm (5.5in) long. **Nocturnal or nighttime types:** Order Strigiformes, the owls (over 130 species). **Largest:** Great eagle owl – 60cm (2ft) long. **Smallest:** Elf owl – 13cm (5in) long.

Birds of prey are adapted to killing sizeable animals. Some are effective hunters, with beaks and claws to kill and tear large prey apart. Others, including many of the largest vultures, are scavengers feeding on the bodies of dead animals. A few feed on insects, snails or fish. Most birds of prey are expert fliers. Some pursue prey at high speed, others are best suited for soaring, sailing through the sky for long periods before homing in on prey or carrion. But many spend much of their life at rest. Their food is nourishing and they do not need frequent meals. If they can hunt efficiently when required, they can also relax when they are not hungry.

Feeding

An osprey is a hawk that catches fish.

Owls, eagles, falcons and hawks kill their prey by grasping with their powerful talons (toes and claws). Their beaks are also powerful, with hooked tips, but are usually reserved for pulling the food apart once it is caught. Vultures feed on carrion and do not need strong claws, but their beaks are strong for tearing flesh. Owls generally swallow prey whole, whereas others tear food into small pieces. The size and type of feet are closely linked to the food the birds eat. An osprey feeds on fish and has sharp scales beneath the toes to hold slippery prey. It has two toes pointing forward and two back. Owls can reverse one toe, but most other birds of prey have three forward toes and one back.

Vultures feeding on the remains of a zebra

Hawk beak

Falcon talon

Flying

Owls have feathers with fringes that make their flight almost silent. Many hunt by sound and their prey also hears well, so silent attack is a big advantage. Some birds of prey rely on speed of flight to catch prey. A peregrine can dive at 320 km/h (200mph). At the other extreme the kestrel can hover over a spot, searching the ground below for possible prey before dropping on it. Short, broad wings allow maneuverability in woods, while long, thin wings permit speed in open country.

A female kestrel hovers, looking for prey.

Senses

Birds of prey have forward-facing eyes that help them to judge distances as they strike at prey. Daytime hunters have very sharp vision, and some may be able to see objects six times smaller or further away than we can. Owls' enormous eyes can see in very dim light. They also have large sensitive ears, which often are a different size on each side of the head. Some pinpoint prey accurately by sound alone. Birds generally have little sense of smell, but vultures can smell carrion from a distance.

An owl has large eyes to see at night.

Hatching

Compared to other birds, some birds of prey lay few eggs. Some of the large eagles lay only one or two eggs in a clutch, and may not lay every year. The incubation period is also long, sometimes a month or more. When the chick is ready to hatch it breaks through the shell using the egg-tooth on the end of its beak. However, the chick still faces a long period of dependence on its parents. A hen bird usually lays her eggs at intervals of a day or so. Many species begin to incubate only when the complete clutch is laid. But birds of prey often incubate from the time the first egg is laid. Thus if there are several eggs, the babies also hatch at intervals. The difference in age is apparent through the nest life, and the oldest and strongest are most likely to survive. A nest of owls may contain youngsters in several stages of growth.

A short-toed eagle hatching from its egg

WATERBIRDS

Major types: Grebes and loons (25 species) swim and dive well. Albatrosses and petrels (90) are oceanic birds. Pelicans, cormorants and relatives (57) fish well. Ducks and geese (150) are mostly freshwater species, gulls and auks (117) seawater. Waders (213) and storks, flamingoes, cranes and rails (197) frequent a variety of habitats.

Many birds make their living in or beside water. There is scarcely a watery habitat, whether it is swamp, lake, river or sea, which is not inhabited by birds. Some, like waders, take their food from the edge of the water or from where the shore is exposed by the tide. Others, such as albatrosses, petrels and auks, spend nearly all their lives at sea, coming to land only to nest. Many waterbirds swim well, propelling themselves with their feet. Others, for instance auks and penguins, use their wings to row underwater. Those that concentrate on diving into the water to feed have well-waterproofed plumage and denser bones than other birds to help them penetrate the water.

Feeding

Waterbirds feed on many different types of food. Several, such as swans and numerous ducks, are vegetarian. They reach below the surface with their beaks for water plants. There are many fish-eaters, often with long pointed beaks to seize prey. Some of them have adaptations to hold slippery prey. For example, the cormorant has a beak with a hooked tip, and the pochard has a beak with a toothed edge. Only one type of bird, the darter, uses its sharp beak as a spear to catch fish. Pelicans, too, have a unique way of scooping up fish, using the big pouch on the lower beak as a fishing net. They sometimes work in groups to round up a shoal of fish. Most fish-eaters swallow prey whole, head first. Flamingoes feed on microscopic plants and animals. They have a sieve-like beak to extract food from the water. They wade in the shallows and dip their head in upside down. Some ducks also sieve for small organisms. Herons also wade, but stalk and wait for larger prey such as fish and frogs, as do some storks. Along the edges of both fresh and sea water, waders such as sandpipers, curlews, plovers and avocets search for food. Some pick up shellfish. Others probe mud at various depths for worms. A few dabble in water for small animals. Among waterbirds competition for food is rarely serious.

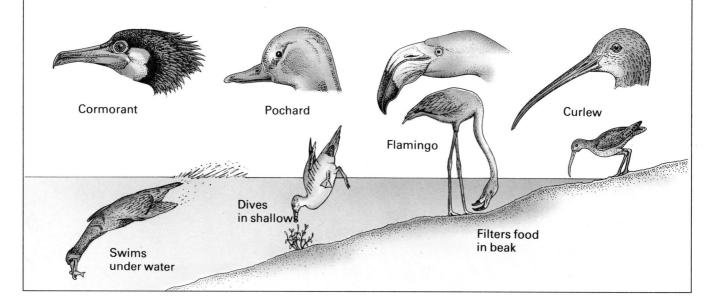

Cormorant

Pochard

Flamingo

Curlew

Dives in shallows

Swims under water

Filters food in beak

Feet

Many birds that wade need to spread their weight to save themselves from sinking into soft mud. They can do this by having long toes or webbing between the toes. The jacana, which walks over lily pads on the surface, has the longest toes of all. A common adaptation among waterbirds that are good swimmers is to have the front three toes joined by webbing, as in ducks and gulls. This provides a large surface with which to push against the water. Cormorants, shags and their relatives have all four toes joined by webbing. Some birds have lobes on their toes instead of a full web. These include the grebes and coots. Birds that propel themselves under water with their wings use webbed feet as rudders.

Great crested grebe   Phalarope   Mallard   Shag

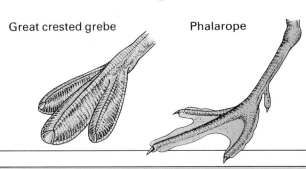
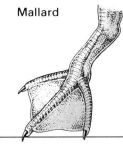
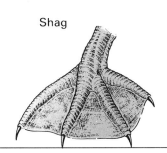

Nests

Waterbirds nest in a variety of ways. Some, such as herons, make a nest of sticks in a tree. Others stay close to the water and make a pile of vegetation to serve as a nest. In species such as coots and grebes, this nest may actually be floating. Many waders and gulls make nests that are little more than a scrape on the ground or a depression in sand or pebbles. Both eggs and young of these birds are usually camouflaged. Some seabirds simply lay eggs on a cliff ledge. These eggs are pointed at one end, so they do not easily roll off.

Puffins nest in crevices on cliff tops.

Mating

Even in the most crowded seabird colonies, parents attend their own chicks and no others. A male and female must recognize one another, stay faithful, and care for their young for the population to survive. In some long-lived birds such as albatrosses, pairs often mate together for life. Outside the breeding season the parents may live apart. Many oceanic species spend most of the year scattered far from land but gather in colonies at favored sites for breeding. Sometimes thousands of birds take over a rocky island.

Courtship display of blue-footed boobies

FLIGHTLESS BIRDS

Major types: Big, running birds – ostrich (1 species), rheas (2), cassowaries (3), emu (1).
Large-bodied, short-legged, nocturnal species – kiwis (3).
Expert swimmers and divers – penguins (16).
Oddities – island rails (about 10).

Considering the advantages of flight, a surprising number of birds are flightless. Often these live in places where there are few enemies on land. On islands dotted around the world are species, closely related to birds that normally fly well, which have lost the power of flight. Then there are species adapted to running, such as rheas and emus. These are so large and swift on foot that they can outrun their enemies. They show some features of the flightless ancestors of modern birds (which evolved from reptiles), such as loose feathers and lack of a large, keeled breastbone. Scientists argue whether in evolution these birds lost the power of flight or whether they ever had it.

Movement

The large running birds have long legs with powerful thigh muscles. They do not perch so have no need of a back toe on the foot, and this has been lost, leaving three front toes. The ostrich has lost another toe, leaving one hoof-like toe and a smaller side one. An ostrich can run at 65 km/h (40mph). When running it may hold its wings out to help it balance. Although penguins cannot take to the air, their wings are not useless. They have evolved as compact paddles used to 'fly' through the water. Penguins are fast in pursuit of prey – some travel so fast in water they can shoot straight out on to a rock high above the sea. Their legs are set far back and are used as rudders.

Incubating

Some of the flightless birds look after their eggs in unusual ways. Male ostriches may mate with several females, which may all lay eggs in one nest. The male takes a large share of incubation. In emus, rheas and cassowaries, it is just the male that incubates the eggs and looks after the young. Some penguins make a nest; others lay single eggs that are held on the feet to incubate.

An ostrich can run quickly.

A penguin dives for fish.

Cassowary incubating eggs

Bird chart

- ● Mostly meat-eating birds
- ● Mostly plant-eating birds

Sulphur-breasted toucan
Ramphastos sulfuratus
S. America, tropical
forest

Canada goose
Branta canadensis
N. America, wetlands

Belted kingfisher
Ceryle alcyon
N. and S. America, near
water

Whooping crane
Grus americana
N. America, swamps.
Rare

Brown pelican
Pelecanus occidentalis
N. and S. America,
coastal waters

Scarlet macaw
Ara macao
S. America, tropical
forest

Mallard
Anas platyrhynchos
Worldwide, mainly
freshwater

Greater flamingo
Phoenicopterus ruber
Americas, Eurasia, Africa,
lakes, lagoons, shores

Bald eagle
Haliaeetus leucocephalus
N. America, near water

Ring-necked pheasant
Phasianus colchicus
Asia, introduced
elsewhere, woodland

Osprey
Pandion haliaetus
Worldwide, near water

King penguin
Aptenodytes patagonica
Cold southern seas

Frigate bird
Fregata magnificens
Tropical oceans

**Crimson topaz
hummingbird**
Topaza pella
S. America, tropical
forest

Wandering albatross
Diomedia exulans
Southorn occanc

Peregrine falcon
Falco peregrinus
Worldwide, open country

Barn swallow
Hirundo rustica
Worldwide, open country

Andean condor
Vultur gryphus
S. America, mountains
and cliffs

Barn owl
Tyto alba
Worldwide, open country

**Red-plumed bird of
paradise**
Paradisaea apoda
New Guinea, tropical
forest

113

Each side of a square represents 150mm (6 inches)

MAMMALS

The three major groups are:
Monotremes- primitive egg-laying animals (3 species).
Marsupials – found in Australasia and South America; the young are born at an undeveloped stage and are often kept in a pouch (266 species).
Placental mammals – the biggest group; young nourished in mother's womb through a placenta. Worldwide.

There are more than 4,000 species of mammals, about half of them belonging to the rodent group, which includes mice and squirrels. Mammals are found in all regions of the world, from the tropics to icy arctic wastes, and have become adapted to all ways of life on land. They include runners, burrowers and climbers. Others fly, or live in the water. Mammals are warm-blooded and have a body covering of hair for insulation. They have an efficient heart and blood system. Most give birth to live young, to which they devote great care. Mammals have a large brain compared to that of most animals, and many are capable of learning much by experience.

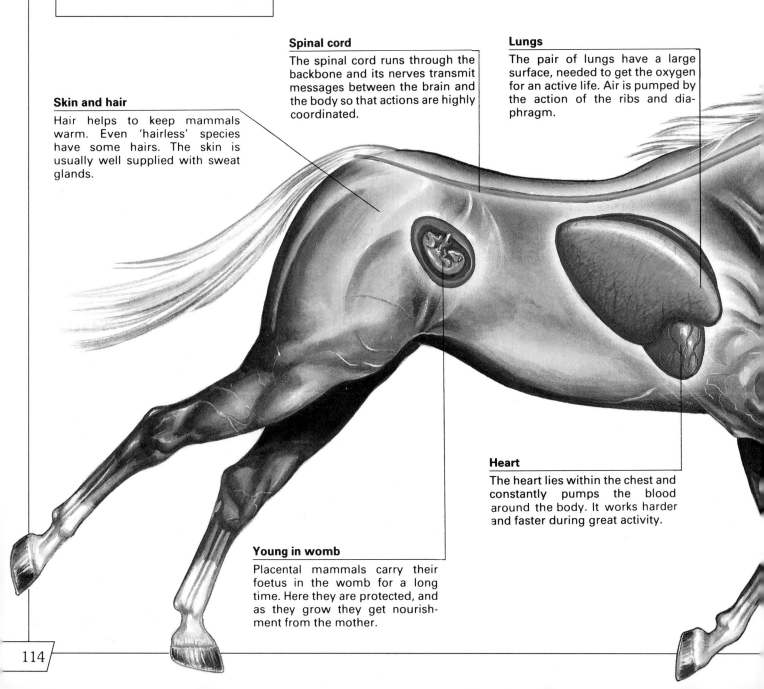

Spinal cord
The spinal cord runs through the backbone and its nerves transmit messages between the brain and the body so that actions are highly coordinated.

Lungs
The pair of lungs have a large surface, needed to get the oxygen for an active life. Air is pumped by the action of the ribs and diaphragm.

Skin and hair
Hair helps to keep mammals warm. Even 'hairless' species have some hairs. The skin is usually well supplied with sweat glands.

Heart
The heart lies within the chest and constantly pumps the blood around the body. It works harder and faster during great activity.

Young in womb
Placental mammals carry their foetus in the womb for a long time. Here they are protected, and as they grow they get nourishment from the mother.

Blood circulation

There is a double circulation. The four-chambered heart pumps blood through the lung and body circuits. Oxygenated (red) and deoxygenated (blue) blood do not mix.

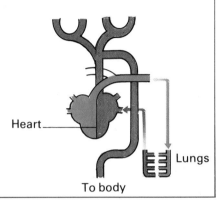

To head

Heart

Lungs

To body

Development and Parental Care

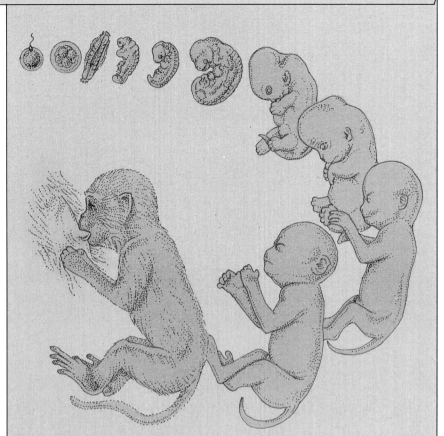

Development starts from a fertilized egg no bigger than a pinhead. This divides into a ball of cells, then becomes attached to the inside of the uterus, or womb, to complete development. The first stages of mammal development are like those of fish, but soon a recognizable baby takes shape. It may then spend much time growing before birth. Some baby mammals, such as those of deer and antelopes, are able to stand and run soon after they are born. Others are born naked and blind. The mother has mammary glands that produce milk as food for the newborn. In some species care by one or both parents may last many years.

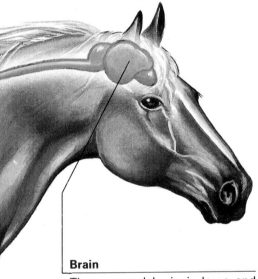

Brain

The mammal brain is large and complex in structure. Much of a mammal's behavior is instinctive but it can also be modified by learning.

Skeleton

Every mammal's skeleton has seven neck vertebrae, but the other bone arrangements are often greatly modified to fit the lifestyle of the species.

PALOMINO HORSE
Equus caballus

HORSE SKELETON

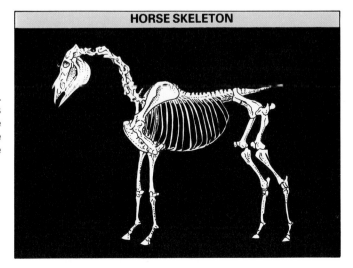

The Mammal World

Present-day land mammals of the world are often divided into groups representing six major geographical regions – the Nearctic, Neotropical, Palaearctic, African, Oriental and Australian. This is based on how the animals are believed to have evolved from common ancestors 200 million years ago, when there was a single landmass on Earth, Pangea. Most of the regions are made up of a single continent, such as Africa and Australia. The Palearctic and Oriental regions are separated mainly by the Himalayas, which act as a barrier to the movements of land animals.

Each region has its own characteristic collection of mammals, well-adapted to the local climate and vegetation. But where there are similar habitats within regions, such as the rain forests and grasslands of South America, Africa and Asia, the same types of mammals – monkeys, big cats and bats, for example – have evolved. Just how unique the mammals of a region are is related to the length of time that part of the world has been separated from the rest. The Australian region became isolated some 70 million years ago, longer than any other and before placental mammals had reached it, and almost all of its native mammals are all marsupials. North America, on the other hand, remained joined to Asia by a land bridge at the Bering Strait. Thus native American mammals are mainly similar to those found in Eurasia.

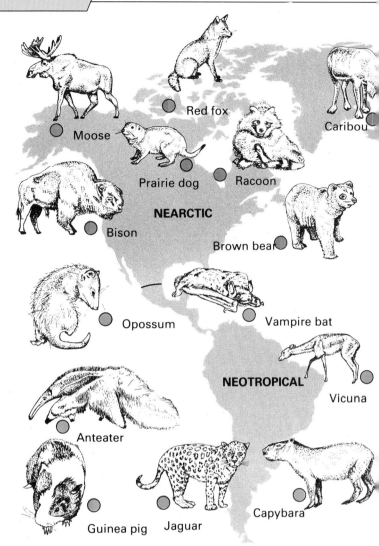

Movement

Among mammals, every method of locomotion is represented. Bats are specially adapted to flying, having front limbs with elongated fingers between which are stretched sheets of skin to form wings. Dolphins, porpoises and whales, along with dugongs and manatees, are adapted to life in water. They have a streamlined body for swimming and front legs modified into paddles. Most carnivores, such as cheetahs, can walk and run fast. Tree-living species, in particular monkeys and apes, can swing from branch to branch, and some can walk on two legs. Flying squirrels and colugos have skin stretched between front and hind limbs that allows them to glide through the air.

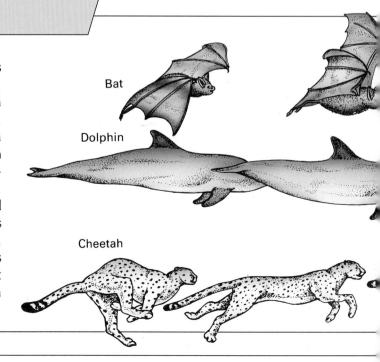

Reindeer

Arctic fox

Polar bear

Hedgehog

PALAEARCTIC

Chiru antelope

Horse

Giant panda

Elephant

Rhinoceros

Elephant

ORIENTAL

Tiger

AFRICAN

Eland

Leopard

Gibbon

Echidna

Kangaroo

Hippopotamus

Orangutan

AUSTRALIAN

Koala

Zebra

Gorilla

Lion

Platypus

Koala

 Animals common to Nearctic and Palaearctic regions

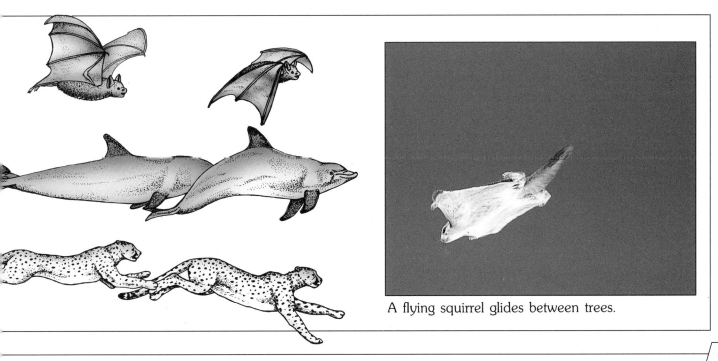

A flying squirrel glides between trees.

POUCHED AND EGG-LAYING

Monotremes: includes only the platypus of Australia and the spiny anteaters of Australia and New Guinea.

Marsupials: about 266 species. Small tree-living opossums (83 species) live in South America. Koalas, kangaroos, numbats, wombats, phalangers, bandicoots and native cats (183) live in the Australian region.

Apart from laying eggs, monotremes differ from other mammals in several ways. They have a lower, more variable body temperature, and the milk glands are modified sweat glands without a true teat. Their skeletons have some reptilian features, and they do not have separate body openings for excretion and reproduction. Marsupials are generally more like the placental mammals, but their mode of reproduction sets them apart. Although giving birth to young at an early stage of development restricts their lifestyle, they do show a wide variety of adaptations and feed on many different types of food. Marsupials include opossums, koalas and kangaroos.

Newborn

The platypus and the spiny anteater lay small leather shelled eggs rather like those of reptiles. The platypus lays its eggs at the end of a burrow in a straw bank in a nest chamber. The spiny anteater develops a pouch during the breeding season, and this provides a temporary home for the eggs and newly hatched young.

With marsupials, the baby remains in the mother's womb for a relatively short time. When it is born its organs are all well formed but few are really working. The baby crawls unaided to one of the mother's teats and seizes it in its mouth. The teat swells, and for a while the baby becomes a fixture into which the mother pumps milk. The baby grows rapidly. In many species a pouch encloses the teats for the young, but in some the teats just lie within a hollow in the abdomen. A newborn marsupial may bear little resemblance to the adult. A baby kangaroo is a thumbnail-sized creature with larger front limbs than back ones, still blind but with a sense of smell to guide it to the pouch. Once it has grown large it may start to leave the pouch for short periods. A new baby may be born when the previous young is becoming independent but still taking milk from the mother.

A duck-billed platypus swimming under water

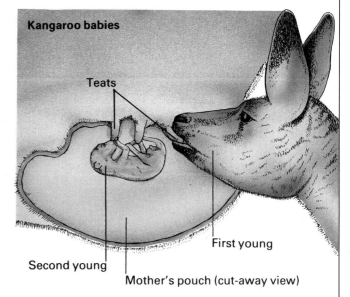

Kangaroo babies

Teats

First young

Second young

Mother's pouch (cut-away view)

Feeding

Koalas feed only on eucalyptus leaves.

A spiny anteater probes the ground for ants.

The familiar kangaroos and wallabies graze grasses or browse on the leaves of shrubs and young trees. Wombats feed on grasses, including the roots, with their constantly growing teeth. Koalas feed in trees on a specialized diet of eucalyptus leaves. Other specialist feeders include the tiny honey opossum, which has a brush-like tongue for lapping up the nectar of flowers. Meat-eaters include the native 'cats' and also a number of insect-eating marsupial 'mice.' The numbat feeds almost exclusively on termites.

All the monotremes (platypus and spiny anteaters) are toothless. The platypus swims well and catches many kinds of small animals with its beak. The spiny anteater can dig well, and licks up ants with its long tongue.

Evolution

Furry warm-blooded creatures resembling present-day mammals first evolved from reptiles during the Age of the Dinosaurs. The egg-layers probably had different ancestors from the other mammals. Some 100 million years ago, before the dinosaurs died out, the first relatives of our marsupial and placental mammals were living, but in a world where the continents were joined more closely than now. Marsupials were able to move from their first home in South America to Australia via Antarctica. Then the continents broke up, leaving most of the marsupials isolated in Australia, with only a few – the opossums – in South America. Evolution has followed a similar path in two, now very separate parts of the world.

Placental

Wolf

California mole

Marsupial

Tasmanian tiger

Marsupial mole

INSECT-EATERS

Major types: The order Insectivora includes moles (47 species), hedgehogs (15) and shrews (over 200). The bats, order Chiroptera, are the second most numerous mammal order, with over 900 species, most adapted to eating insects. Other insect-eaters include pangolins (7), South American anteaters (4) and armadillos (20).

The very first mammals to evolve were insect-eaters. Present-day shrews look similar to some of these early mammals and, like them, have small sharp teeth in their jaws to catch and chop insects and other small animals. Insect-eating remains a very successful way of life and shrews and their relatives are found almost worldwide. Insect-eating bats are another ancient group. They developed the ability to fly 50 million years ago and have been successfully eating the huge supply of flying insects ever since. Ants and termites are another large food source, and unrelated animals of many groups, including anteaters and armadillos, rely on them as their staple diet.

Feeding

Mammals with small bodies lose heat fast. Tiny hunters like shrews feed voraciously to obtain the energy to make up for this heat loss. They eat about their own body weight daily, sometimes even more. They constantly scurry through the undergrowth and leaf litter, pouncing on beetles, centipedes and spiders. Hedgehogs also feed on a variety of insects and slugs, but being larger can take life more slowly. Moles move through their network of underground tunnels, picking up worms and other juicy morsels. For pangolins, aardvarks and other anteaters food comes in very tiny packets. Large claws to break into nests, and a long sticky tongue to lick up large numbers very quickly, are more important than biting, and these animals have small simple teeth or none. Insect-eating bats have sharp teeth to seize and bite their food. Many use their wings to help gather their prey in flight. Some pick prey from leaves, others swoop over water to hunt.

A long-eared bat hunting a moth

Worms are a favorite food of European moles.

Active period

Shrews need so much food that they are active most of the day, but alternate periods of activity with short periods of rest. Bats, although they have a tiny body and a large surface, are not constantly active. They emerge at night to feed on nocturnal insects. During the day they hang at rest upside down and allow their body temperature to drop, so conserving energy until the night's activity.

Hundreds of bats emerging at sunset

Senses

Underground, moles have little use for eyes but their senses of hearing and smell are good. Their sense of touch is clearly important too, as can be seen from the large whiskers they have. Shrews have poor eyesight. In bats, too, eyesight is not very important. Insect-eating bats have such acute hearing that they are able to navigate and chase prey by listening to echoes of their own high-pitched voices.

A shrew sniffs the air for possible danger.

Hibernation

In the tropics there are usually insects available for most of the year, but in temperate regions there may be plenty in summer but few in winter. Shrews stay active all year but in winter have a hard time and many die. Hedgehogs solve the problem by hibernating. They find an undisturbed frost-free place and settle down to sleep, allowing the body temperature to drop very low. They stay barely alive – their hearts beat slowly and they scarcely breathe. Sometimes they wake and move from their nests, but in winter they are inactive, saving energy by not trying to stay 'warm-blooded.' Bats also hibernate during the coldest months.

A European hedgehog hibernating in a nest of leaves

RODENTS AND RABBITS

Within the order Rodentia there are 3 main groups: Squirrel group, with kangaroo rats, marmots and beavers (377 species). Porcupine group, with African mole-rats and, from South America, guinea pigs, chinchillas (188). Mouse group, with rats, hamsters and jerboas (over 1,137). The order Lagomorpha includes rabbits, hares and pikas (58 species).

Rodents, a group that includes mice, rats and rabbits, are extremely successful mammals, found in nearly all habitats except the sea. Most live on the ground, although there are many – such as squirrels – that are good at climbing or living in trees. Others, like beavers and some voles, live in and around fresh water. Many use burrows for shelters and homes, but mole-rats and other species are adapted to a life burrowing underground and almost never come to the surface. The secrets of their success include their feeding methods and the ability of almost all, to reproduce fast. Hares, rabbits and the similar pikas share some of the same adaptations but are not so varied.

Teeth and jaws

Rodents have a pair of large incisor teeth at the top and bottom of the front of the mouth. These grow continuously, and are used for gnawing into tough plant food, a process that wears the teeth down as fast as they grow. The enamel on the front of the incisors is hardest, so the teeth wear into a chisel shape. Along the side of the jaws are flattened chewing teeth. Rabbits have two pairs of chisel-shaped incisor teeth. They make good use of food by passing it through the gut twice, eating the feces produced the first time.

A porcupine shows its long front incisors.

Breeding

Many rodents produce great numbers of offspring. This is not so much because their litters are large – while some species produce as many as 17 young at a time, a more typical number is 4 – but because the young themselves become able to breed at an early age. In species such as mice, pregnancy lasts just a few weeks and those less than a year old may start to produce litters. In favorable conditions populations build up fast. Rabbits, too, breed fast. With no deaths, the offspring of a single pair could reach 33 million in 3 years.

House mice produce litters several times a year.

Homes

Rodents make their homes in a variety of places. Many climbing species rest in tree holes. Others make a ball nest from sticks, as do some squirrels, or from grasses or bark, as do harvest mice and dormice. Most rodent homes are not elaborate, but wood rats and stick-nest rats build large mounds of twigs to serve as weatherproof houses. These may have several compartments, including a place to store food and a latrine. The most elaborate aboveground structures are made by beavers, which make dams of sticks and mud to control water levels around the 'lodge' containing the family. Many rodents seek refuge down burrows. Some construct complex systems of tunnels with escape holes, nest chambers, storage places and latrines. Prairie dogs build a raised lip of soil around the entrance to keep out floodwater. The longest tunnels are those of mole-rats – more than 400m (440yd) long. The homes of rabbits are similar but less varied.

A beaver's dam and lodge in Alaska

Squirrels sometimes nest in holes in trees.

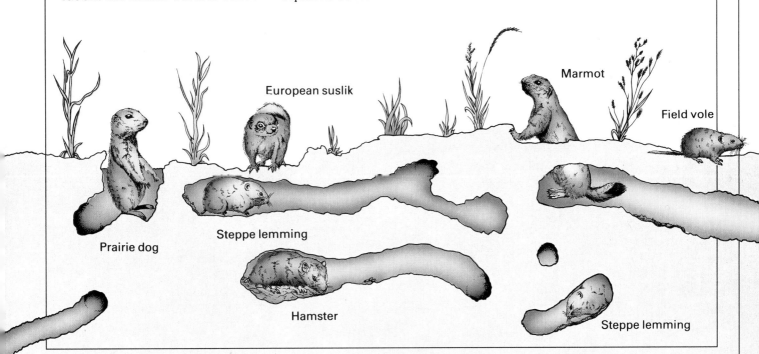

European suslik

Marmot

Field vole

Prairie dog

Steppe lemming

Hamster

Steppe lemming

WHALES AND PORPOISES

There are 2 major types:
Toothed whales (66 species), including river dolphins, beaked whales, dolphins and porpoises.
Whalebone (baleen) whales (10 species), including gray whale, rorquals and right whales.
Biggest species: Blue whale – more than 30m (100ft) long and weighing 140 tons.

Whales and their relatives the dolphins comprise mammals completely adapted to life in water. The majority of the 80 or so species live in the open seas, and of these, many inhabit warm tropical waters, while others spend much of their lives in the cool polar seas. All are mammals that during evolution returned to the sea, where animal life began. They still have a fish-like appearance. Among them are the biggest animals ever to have lived on Earth, with the Blue whale at 140 tons. Whales have no hind limbs or external ears. Their forelimbs take the form of paddles, and they have a tail with flukes. Beneath the skin is a layer of blubber, or fat, which helps to conserve body heat in the water.

Breathing

Some whales can stay under water for an hour or more. Yet they breathe air with their lungs and must surface to replace the oxygen their bodies need. They store oxygen in their muscles and on a dive use this and the oxygen in their lungs to stay alive. As they surface, they open the blowhole on top of their head and blow out the used air. Then they take one or more deep breaths. Underwater, the blowhole is closed by a valve and the windpipe is sealed off from the throat to prevent water entering the lungs when the animal feeds.

A fin whale blows water out of its blowhole.

Birth

Most whales do not reach maturity for many years. Pregnancy lasts from 8 months, for small dolphins, to 16 months or more for the big whales such as the blue, fin and sperm whales. Mostly only one offspring is produced. The baby is born under water tail-first. Immediately it surfaces, or its mother nudges its head out of the water, to take its first breath. The baby suckles milk from nipples hidden in folds on the mother's underside. Care of the young lasts weeks or months and is often carried out by all the females in a group.

A mother dolphin and her offspring

Feeding

Whales are divided into two main groups by the different types of jaws and feeding methods.

Toothed whales have narrow lower jaws and, as adults, cone-shaped pointed teeth in the lower or both jaws. The teeth number from 2 to 200 depending on the species. In nar-whals, one of the two upper-jaw teeth is greatly enlarged to form a spirally twisted tusk 2m (6.5ft) in length in the males. Toothed whales feed mainly on fish and squid.

Baleen, or whalebone, whales lack teeth and the upper jaw has up to 300 plates of horny material similar to matted hair or fingernails. These plates of baleen hang down from the jaw and act as strainers to sift out plankton, the tiny aquatic animals and plants. When baleen whales are not feeding, the plates are enclosed within the broad lower jaw.

A southern right whale feeding on plankton

A killer whale hunts in the Arctic Ocean.

Migration

There tend to be many separate populations of whales. Some inhabit just the Northern Hemisphere, others the Southern, and within each there are Pacific, Atlantic and Indian Ocean groups. Within each area, groups of whales may migrate many thousands of miles each year, following definite circuits. These sometimes take them close to the mainland or among the pack ice of polar regions. Most toothed whales migrate to keep up with the movements of the fish on which they feed. Baleen whales, move towards the poles in summer and return to the tropics in winter for the breeding season.

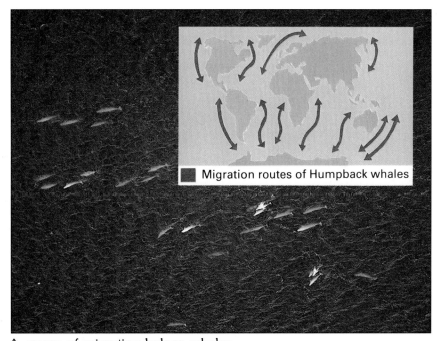

Migration routes of Humpback whales

A group of migrating beluga whales

Major types: Odd-toed – includes tapirs and rhinos (9 species), horses, asses and zebras (7). Even-toed – includes pigs (9), hippos (2), camels (6), deer (37), cattle and antelope (121), giraffe (2). **Related to these:** seacows (4), elephants (2), hyraxes (11).

One of the main common body features of non-fish vertebrates is the possession of two pairs of limbs, each bearing five digits (fingers or toes). In mammals these so-called pentadactyl limbs (from the Greek *penta* five, *dactyl* finger) have, during evolution, taken on such forms as the wings of bats and the flippers of seals or, as in dugongs and manatees, a pair has been lost. Hoofed mammals are generally medium-sized to large plant-eating animals in which finger and toe nails have become large, flat and greatly toughened as hooves. Hooves allow the animals to walk on their digits rather than on the soles of their feet as humans do, and allow good balance while running.

Hooves

There are two main groups of hoofed animals – odd-toed and even-toed. The odd-toed species have a variable number of digits on each foot but almost always three or one. For example, rhinoceroses have three, whereas horses have just one large central digit on each foot. Tapirs have four on the front feet and three on the hind feet. The weight of these animals is carried by the central digit or digits of each foot. Even-toed species have two or four digits on each foot. The more primitive kinds, such as pigs and peccaries, tend to have four digits per foot yet they rest their weight and walk on only two of these, usually the third and fourth. Camels, and the South American llama, guanaco and alpaca, have feet with two equal digits. Elephants have five digits per foot and these are spread out to support the animals' weight almost equally.

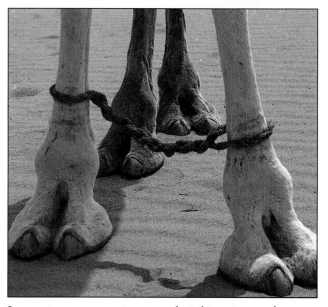

Large toes prevent a camel sinking in sand.

Horse	Pronghorn	Camel	Rhinoceros	Hippopotamus	Elephant

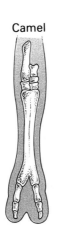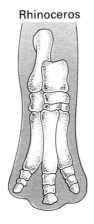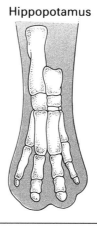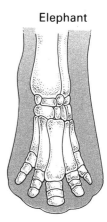

Digestion

Even-toed mammals are adapted to eating lots of plant material, ranging from roots to leaves and fruits. Pigs and their relatives, however, eat both plant and animal food. But they all have cheek teeth specialized for grinding vegetable material and a stomach that has several chambers for processing food in various ways. One group, which includes deer, giraffe, cattle and sheep, are called the cud chewers. Cud is food that is first stored in the stomach then returned to the mouth for chewing thoroughly. These animals are called ruminants. Odd-toed mammals also have grinding cheek teeth but the stomach is simple in structure and none of them chews the cud.

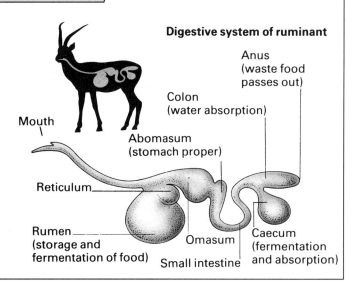

Digestive system of ruminant

Mouth

Reticulum

Rumen (storage and fermentation of food)

Omasum

Small intestine

Abomasum (stomach proper)

Colon (water absorption)

Anus (waste food passes out)

Caecum (fermentation and absorption)

Feeding

In the vast grasslands of Africa, South America and Eurasia there are large populations of various hoofed mammals living side by side. There is little competition for food between them because the different species do not have the same diet. In the Serengeti Plains of Africa, for example, zebras and rhinoceroses eat the short grass. Elands feed on the leaves of shrubs and young trees. Elephants use their long flexible trunk to strip leaves and bark from the upper branches of trees. Giraffes, with their long neck, can stretch even higher, above all the other plant-eaters, and reach leaves at the very top of tall trees.

Giraffe

Cape buffalo

Cape eland

Impala

Elephant

Gerenuk

Zebra

Wildebeest

White rhinoceros

Family life

Many hoofed mammals feed, sleep and travel across country in herds. Within these herds are several family groups. Elephants occasionally collect in the hundreds but usually move in herds of about 40 in which each member is related to all the others. The small herds consist of mothers and their young, sisters, cousins and aunts. Male elephants travel singly or in small all-male groups. Members of family herds communicate with one another by calls and scents. Living as a herd offers protection from enemies and allows the young to learn about their surroundings from elders.

A baby African elephant only three days old

Weapons

Where resources such as food or homes are limited, many animals of a species compete with one another. Some have evolved weapons to improve fighting ability in contests. Warthogs and elephants bear tusks, which are greatly enlarged teeth, and use them as battering rams. Various antelopes and their relatives, such as ibexes, duikers and waterbuck, have horns for jabbing and which they lock together and try and twist each other's heads down on to the ground. Similarly, most male deer grow branched antlers, which are bony outgrowths of the skull, and interlock these with those of their opponents as they try and push one another over. Antlers are shed each year while horns are permanent.

Male bighorn sheep fighting with their horns

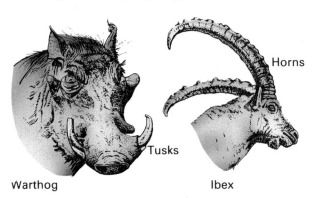
Tusks

Warthog

Horns

Ibex

Antlers

Reindeer

128

Mating

The reproductive behavior of hoofed mammals has been studied for centuries because the successful breeding of species such as sheep, goats, cattle and horses is the basis of domestication and animal farming. In the wild, females are 'in heat' – that is, ready to mate – at only certain times of the year, and in several species males and females live apart for many months then come together briefly for mating. Males of some species often compete with one another for the right to mate with females and have many 'wives.' Pregnancy generally lasts many months, and only one offspring is produced at a time. Domesticated animals, though, are bred to come in heat more than once a year and for multiple births.

American wild mustangs mating

Life in the water

Seacows, the dugong and manatees, like whales, are adapted to an aquatic way of life. They have a massive cigar-shaped body, paddle-like front legs, no hind legs, and have a flattened tail. To help conserve heat they have a thick layer of blubber. They spend all their lives in water, feeding, sleeping, mating and giving birth beneath the surface. They breathe through their nostrils on top of their rounded muzzle, surfacing frequently to replenish the air in their lungs.

Yet seacows are often grouped with hoofed mammals, with elephants and hyraxes as their closest relatives, because many have front legs with flattened horny nails. The dugong lives in warm waters off the coasts of South America, Southeast Asia and Australia. It is hairless and the male bears a pair of tusks. Manatees frequent estuaries of the Atlantic coasts of North America and Seacows are placid, sluggish animals that feed on plants such as eelgrass.

A heavy hippo can swim more easily than walk.

A manatee in a Florida river

MEAT-EATERS

Major types: Cat family (35 species), including lions, tigers, wild and domestic small cats. Dog family (35), including jackal, fennec, wolf, fox. Bears (7), raccoons and pandas (17), civet family (80) and weasel family (67). Seals, sea lions, walrus (33).

There are some 300 species of mammal that live on a substantial meat diet. They are known as carnivores. Some, such as lions and tigers, are predators, hunting live prey. Others, among them hyenas, are scavengers, taking the remains of other animals' kills. However, giant pandas feed almost exclusively on bamboo shoots, and aardwolves on carrion as well as insects. Closely related to true carnivores are seals, sea lions and the walrus, which are adapted to life in water. They feed mainly on fish and shellfish. Common to carnivores are strong jaws with large canine teeth and cheek teeth with cutting edges that slice against each other to tear and chew flesh.

Hunting

Most carnivores are solitary creatures and hunt for prey alone. A tiger, for example, stalks its prey then, when within striking distance, rushes at it. It knocks the animal down to the ground then grabs its throat in its powerful jaws. The prey, unable to breathe, dies quickly. Wolves and other members of the dog family hunt in packs of up to 30. They often surround an animal then close in for the kill. Weasels and stoats often chase their prey into underground burrows, and otters pounce on fish swimming in shallow water. Walruses do not hunt but rake up shellfish from the sea bed.

Wolves hunt together in packs.

Feeding

Big cats such as lions, cheetahs, panthers and tigers gorge on their kill in one meal and may not feed again for many days. Scavengers such as jackals eat whenever food is available but tend to look for a carcass each day. They have particularly strong cheek teeth that allow them to crack open bones to feed on the rich marrow inside. Carnivores such as bears and raccoons are omnivorous, having a mixed diet of animal and plant food. The brown bear will eat fish, carrion, plant food and, like the red fox, where it lives close to people will raid garbage cans for scraps of food.

A female tiger eating her prey

Scents and signals

Most carnivores except seals possess a pair of glands near their tail from which they can squirt a strong-smelling liquid. They use this scent to mark out their territory, attract a mate, or as a means of defense. To define their territories, wild cats and dogs spray scent on tree trunks and rocks around the boundaries. Female tigers, when ready to mate, use their scent to attract males, who then compete with one another for the female's favor. Skunks, when threatened, squirt their foul-smelling scent. They can squirt as far as 3m (10ft) and the scent is so bad that the attacker runs off. Civets produce a sweet-smelling scent, musk, that is used for perfumes.

A lynx marking its territory with scent

Breeding

A female cat or dog often mates with many males, a female otter or badger with just one. Among weasels, stoats and polecats, the females are often smaller than the males and become ready to mate at only one, regular time of the year. After mating, the fertilized egg does not immediately become attached to the wall of the mother's womb and grow. This is delayed so that the young will be born at a time of year when food is more likely to be plentiful. At mating time among seals, males and pregnant females haul themselves out on land. The much larger males fight fiercely for the females. Mating takes place a few days after pupping.

Male walruses will fight for mates.

MONKEYS AND APES

Major types: Most primitive types – tree shrews (18 species), lemurs (15), indri and sifakas (4), lorises, pottos, bush babies (10), tarsiers (3). New World monkeys (41) – tamarins, marmosets, spider monkeys. Old World monkeys (82) – langurs, baboons, colobuses. Apes (14) – gibbons, orangutan, chimpanzee, gorilla.

The first mammals to evolve were insect-eating, ground-living animals. One group of these gradually became adapted to living in trees. From these arose monkeys and apes and their relatives, which include small tree shrews and tarsiers, but also humans. They are often called primates, from the Latin *primus* meaning first or of the highest rank, because these mammals are the most highly developed of all animals. They have a large complex brain and keen senses of touch, hearing and vision. The eyes are set on the front of the head to give stereoscopic vision. The skeleton is unspecialized, with all limbs having five digits. Primates have adapted to many different forest habitats.

Movement

All primates show adaptations to living in trees. Stereoscopic vision is needed to judge distances accurately, as when leaping from tree to tree. Most New World monkeys have a prehensile tail, one that can grasp a branch to help cling to a tree. Most primates have hands and feet that can grasp objects well. They use them not only for movement but also to take fruit, leaves and insect grubs, which form the diet of most species. Indri and sifakas have longer legs than arms. They cling to trees in an upright position and, like lemurs, move on the ground by hopping. Gibbons have longer arms than legs and use them to swing between branches. Chimpanzees have evolved an upright stance and they can walk on two legs. Such adaptations, however, have restricted the range of non-human primates to tropical and subtropical forests and tree and grass areas.

Gibbon

Chimpanzee

Tarsier

Lemur

Diana monkey

Social life

The higher primates are mostly sociable animals living in family groups within feeding territories. They travel together across country or through the trees, usually for protection, with the females and their babies in the center of the group. Among species such as baboons and chimps, the young learn, mostly through play, to respect their elders and to know their place.

Grooming plays an important part in maintaining the status system within the group.

Chimpanzees with baby

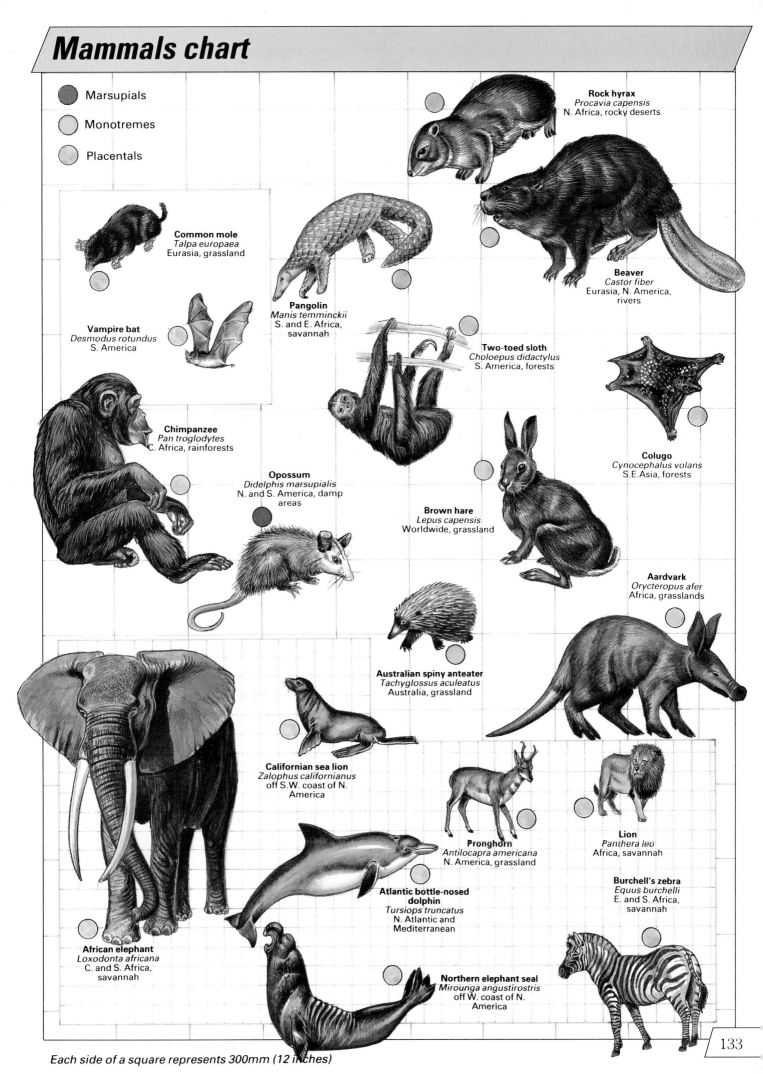

Mammals chart

- ● Marsupials
- ○ Monotremes
- ○ Placentals

Common mole
Talpa europaea
Eurasia, grassland

Vampire bat
Desmodus rotundus
S. America

Chimpanzee
Pan troglodytes
C. Africa, rainforests

Pangolin
Manis temminckii
S. and E. Africa,
savannah

Opossum
Didelphis marsupialis
N. and S. America, damp
areas

Rock hyrax
Procavia capensis
N. Africa, rocky deserts

Beaver
Castor fiber
Eurasia, N. America,
rivers

Two-toed sloth
Choloepus didactylus
S. America, forests

Brown hare
Lepus capensis
Worldwide, grassland

Colugo
Cynocephalus volans
S.E.Asia, forests

Australian spiny anteater
Tachyglossus aculeatus
Australia, grassland

Aardvark
Orycteropus afer
Africa, grasslands

Californian sea lion
Zalophus californianus
off S.W. coast of N.
America

Pronghorn
Antilocapra americana
N. America, grassland

**Atlantic bottle-nosed
dolphin**
Tursiops truncatus
N. Atlantic and
Mediterranean

Lion
Panthera leo
Africa, savannah

Burchell's zebra
Equus burchelli
E. and S. Africa,
savannah

African elephant
Loxodonta africana
C. and S. Africa,
savannah

Northern elephant seal
Mirounga angustirostris
off W. coast of N.
America

133

Each side of a square represents 300mm (12 inches)

LIVING HABITATS & COMMUNITIES

CONTENTS

INTRODUCTION

Every part of the the Earth – from the tundra to the tropics, and mountaintop to ocean floor – is teeming with life. At any particular time, all of Earth's life forms – plants and animals are in balance with each other and with the soil, air and water around them. In a living community, any change in one species affects many others. It is a delicate balance, and a change in any one factor brings about changes in others.

One of the biggest influences on the balance of nature is the activity of human beings. We are changing the environment too fast for many plants and animals to adapt to the changes. People chop down trees and the exposed soil is washed away. And because trees release oxygen into the air, it is not only the forest plants and animals that may ultimately be affected. The oxygen in the Earth's atmosphere – something that all organisms depend on – is being reduced as huge areas forest are cleared for roads and agriculture. A greater awareness of the various factors that have led to the extinction of many species can help to save the life forms that remain.

Many plants rely on animals for pollination and seed dispersal, just as animals need plants for food and shelter. Scientists estimate that whenever a species of plant becomes extinct, about 30 animals – mostly small invertebrates – also become extinct because, directly or indirectly, their lives depended on that plant.

In 1982, a biologist working in a tropical forest found 600 new insect species in just one type of tree.

All living systems are the product of evolution, a very slow and probably gradual process of change that can produce new species of all kinds of organisms – both plant and animal. Evolution is going on all the time, but too slowly for us to notice it. In a living community, any change in one species affects many others, because their lives are all interlinked. So relationships that exist today are the result of a long process of evolving together.

Eventually, this kind of coevolution can lead to specialists, such as the yucca moth and the yucca weevil, with only one food source. Or it can produce generalists, like the cactus wren, able to eat a wide range of foods. When there is a sudden change in the climate, specialists suffer badly; if the yucca trees die out so will the yucca moth. Generalists tend to evolve into new species adapted to the new conditions.

Living systems

Biologists divide the natural world into smaller units they can study. The smallest unit is an individual organism. It belongs to a population – all the members of that species living within the area. The species also forms part of a community – all the different organisms in the area. The next level is the ecosystem, which includes the community as well as the soil, water and other non-living features. Biologists also try to identify the different types of organisms in an ecosystem – herbivores, carnivores and decomposers. They aim to work out how they interact today, and how they have evolved together to produce the present ecosystem. They recognize many distinctive types of ecosystems and call these biomes. Broadleaved woodland is just one type; others include desert, coral reef and tropical rainforest.

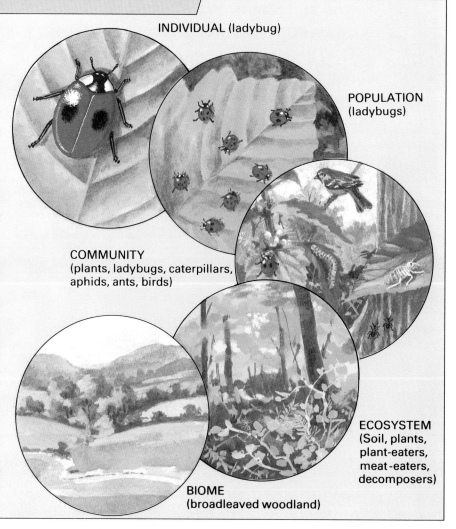

INDIVIDUAL (ladybug)

POPULATION (ladybugs)

COMMUNITY
(plants, ladybugs, caterpillars, aphids, ants, birds)

ECOSYSTEM
(Soil, plants, plant-eaters, meat-eaters, decomposers)

BIOME
(broadleaved woodland)

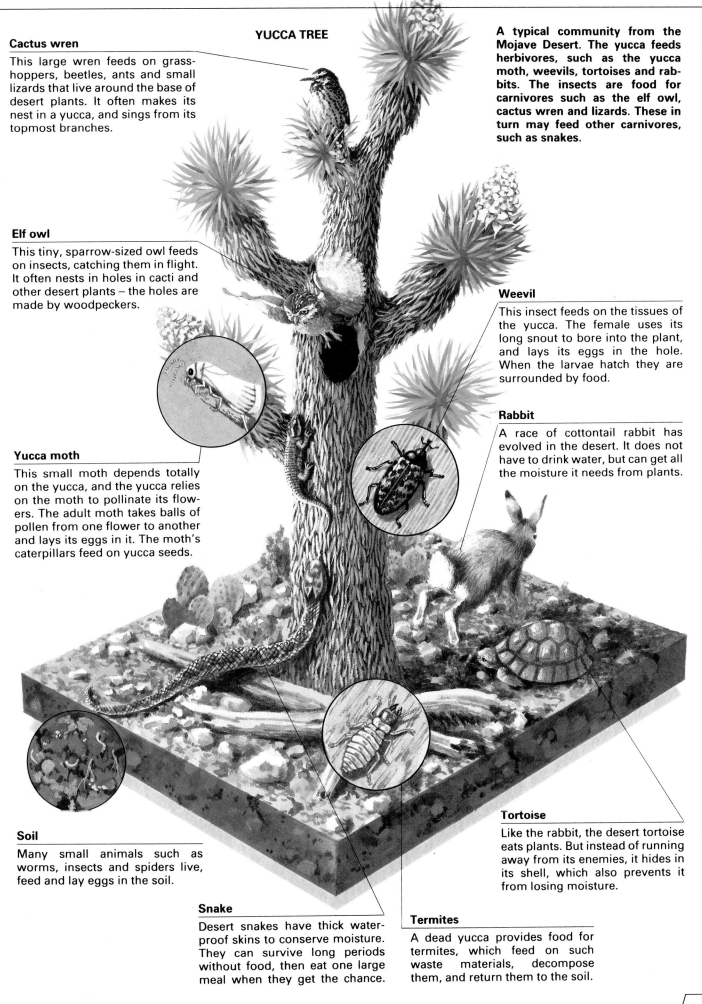

Cactus wren

This large wren feeds on grass-hoppers, beetles, ants and small lizards that live around the base of desert plants. It often makes its nest in a yucca, and sings from its topmost branches.

YUCCA TREE

A typical community from the Mojave Desert. The yucca feeds herbivores, such as the yucca moth, weevils, tortoises and rabbits. The insects are food for carnivores such as the elf owl, cactus wren and lizards. These in turn may feed other carnivores, such as snakes.

Elf owl

This tiny, sparrow-sized owl feeds on insects, catching them in flight. It often nests in holes in cacti and other desert plants – the holes are made by woodpeckers.

Weevil

This insect feeds on the tissues of the yucca. The female uses its long snout to bore into the plant, and lays its eggs in the hole. When the larvae hatch they are surrounded by food.

Rabbit

A race of cottontail rabbit has evolved in the desert. It does not have to drink water, but can get all the moisture it needs from plants.

Yucca moth

This small moth depends totally on the yucca, and the yucca relies on the moth to pollinate its flowers. The adult moth takes balls of pollen from one flower to another and lays its eggs in it. The moth's caterpillars feed on yucca seeds.

Soil

Many small animals such as worms, insects and spiders live, feed and lay eggs in the soil.

Snake

Desert snakes have thick water-proof skins to conserve moisture. They can survive long periods without food, then eat one large meal when they get the chance.

Termites

A dead yucca provides food for termites, which feed on such waste materials, decompose them, and return them to the soil.

Tortoise

Like the rabbit, the desert tortoise eats plants. But instead of running away from its enemies, it hides in its shell, which also prevents it from losing moisture.

RELATIONSHIPS

Parasites live on or in the body of another organism. The largest is the tapeworm, which grows up to 12m (40 ft) long inside its host's intestines. A tapeworm in a whale was found to be 30m (nearly 100ft) long. A whipworm produces more than 1,000 eggs every day for 6-8 years.

Coevolution results in many interesting relationships between species. Often different plants and animals compete for the same resource. The effects of this can be seen in forests, where the trees grow very tall because they are competing for the light. Other organisms, such as predator and prey, are in direct conflict, as each strives to survive. Some, such as fleas, are parasites that live totally at the expense of their host. And in symbiosis, two species live together – in some cases for their mutual benefit, and in others for the benefit of only one species rather than the other.

Predators and prey

When predators chase their prey, it is usually the slowest prey animals that get caught. So evolution has continued to produce faster-running animals, until some sort of limit is reached (an animal's legs can only be so long). The predators are forced to evolve in a similar way, and the result is a "biological arms race." Some prey animals rely on strong defenses, such as a hard shell or thick leathery skin to protect them from predators. In this sort of arms race, the predator tends to develop long stabbing teeth or powerful claws to overcome such defenses.

The pheasant is a common prey of the red fox.

Parasites

Parasites are organisms that live on or in another organism (the host) and rely on it for their food. They occur among all forms of life. Microscopic disease-causing bacteria and viruses are parasites. Larger parasites include blood-sucking insects such as lice and fleas, sap-sucking aphids and weevils (insects that are parasites on plants), and worms such as tapeworms that live in the host's intestines. Parasitic plants are easy to recognize because they usually lack chlorophyll and so are not green. They get all their food from the host plant, and do not need to photosynthesize.

The parasitic dodder twines around other plants.

Give and take

When aphids feed on plant sap they get far more sugar than they need, because sap contains a lot more sugar than protein. So the aphids get rid of the excess sugar in a sticky liquid called honeydew. The aphids are helpless against predators such as ladybugs. Ants are not and can drive away many of the aphids' enemies. The aphids benefit from the ants presence so to encourage the ants, aphids store up the honeydew in their bodies and release it only when ants stroke them. This is an example of mutualism – a close relationship in which both species benefit.

Another type of relationship is commensalism, in which only one of the species benefits. But it does so without causing any harm to the other one. A common example is a small animal that feeds on the scraps left over from a larger animal's meals.

Ants collecting honeydew from black aphids

Decomposers

Feeding on dead things and biological waste products is a small army of decomposers, or saprotrophs. Without them the world would soon be knee-deep in dead matter. One important group of decomposers are molds and fungi, most of which live in this way. Many grow on dead trees and other plant waste (such as rotten fruit). Although fungi are usually decomposers, some also grow on live trees that have been weakened in some way – in other words, they can switch from being decomposers to being parasites when the right opportunity arises. Other decomposers are dung beetles, which bury balls of dung along with their eggs to provide food for the young when they hatch. Carrion beetles do the same thing with carcasses of dead animals.

A dung beetle rolling a ball of antelope dung

Most toadstools live on decaying vegetation.

HABITATS

Tropical forests cover 10 per cent of the Earth's surface area, and boreal coniferous forests cover another 10 per cent. Desert and tundra together cover about a quarter of the total land surface, but account for only 2 per cent of the total weight of plants.

Around the North and South Poles it is too cold for any plants to grow. At the equator where the temperatures are highest, dense forest covers most of the land. In between the poles and the equator there is a gradual change in vegetation as the climate gets warmer. If things were that simple, a vegetation map of the world would just have a series of horizontal bands. But there is another important factor: rainfall. Because of the way winds blow around the globe, some regions get very little rain and have become deserts. Areas that are dry part of the year have scrub or savanna vegetation.

Some types of vegetation are found only in the Northern Hemisphere because there is no land at the corresponding latitude south of the equator.

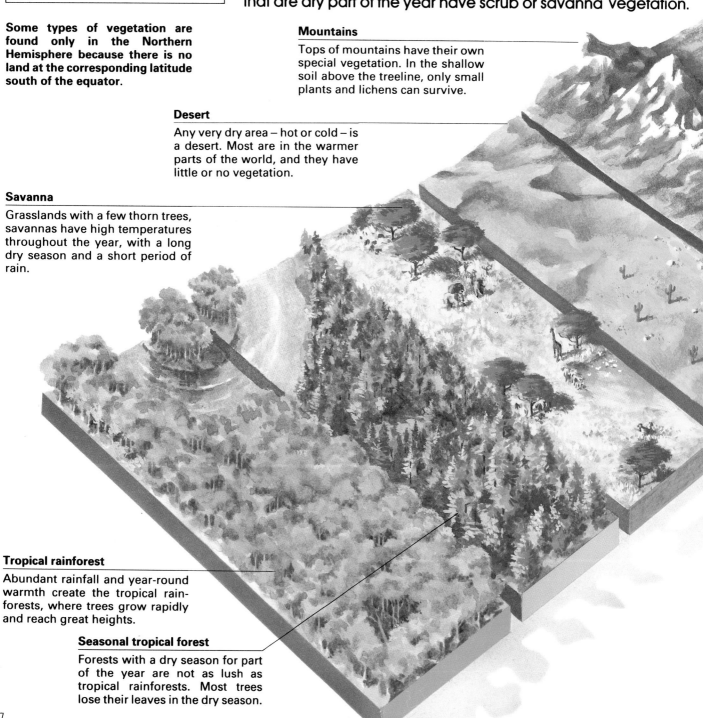

Mountains

Tops of mountains have their own special vegetation. In the shallow soil above the treeline, only small plants and lichens can survive.

Desert

Any very dry area – hot or cold – is a desert. Most are in the warmer parts of the world, and they have little or no vegetation.

Savanna

Grasslands with a few thorn trees, savannas have high temperatures throughout the year, with a long dry season and a short period of rain.

Tropical rainforest

Abundant rainfall and year-round warmth create the tropical rain-forests, where trees grow rapidly and reach great heights.

Seasonal tropical forest

Forests with a dry season for part of the year are not as lush as tropical rainforests. Most trees lose their leaves in the dry season.

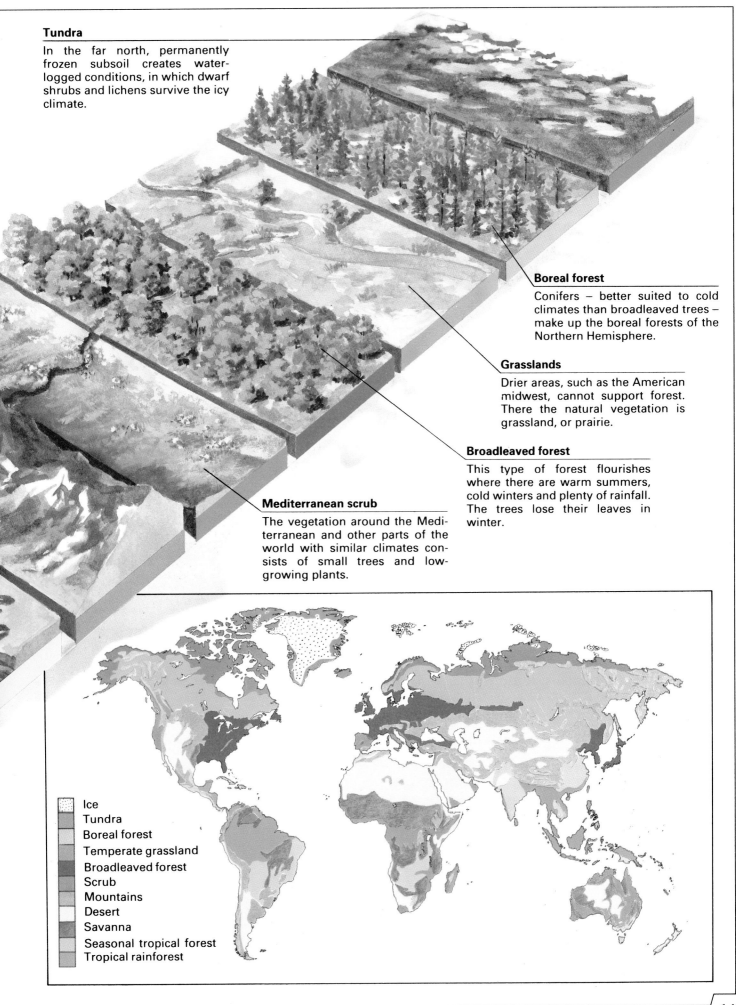

Tundra

In the far north, permanently frozen subsoil creates water-logged conditions, in which dwarf shrubs and lichens survive the icy climate.

Boreal forest

Conifers — better suited to cold climates than broadleaved trees — make up the boreal forests of the Northern Hemisphere.

Grasslands

Drier areas, such as the American midwest, cannot support forest. There the natural vegetation is grassland, or prairie.

Broadleaved forest

This type of forest flourishes where there are warm summers, cold winters and plenty of rainfall. The trees lose their leaves in winter.

Mediterranean scrub

The vegetation around the Mediterranean and other parts of the world with similar climates consists of small trees and low-growing plants.

Ice
Tundra
Boreal forest
Temperate grassland
Broadleaved forest
Scrub
Mountains
Desert
Savanna
Seasonal tropical forest
Tropical rainforest

Savanna

Savanna consists of grassland with a few scattered trees, mainly acacias, or thorn trees, which can withstand the dry season. Fire is an important factor. When everything is tinder-dry, fires start naturally, and many plants have special adaptations to survive fires and grow again.

The best-known savannas are the extensive grasslands of Africa. Many grazing animals, such as zebras and antelopes, live there and are preyed on by carnivores such as lions and leopards. As the dry season approaches, vast herds of grazers such as wildebeest migrate thousands of miles to find food. When the rain comes and the lush new grass grows, the animals migrate back again to take advantage of the food supply.

A herd of zebras on the African savanna

Deserts

Desert regions vary widely. Most are extremely hot (at least in the daytime), but some, such as the deserts of Mongolia, are very cold. Even deserts like the Sahara are cold at night. For this reason, the plants and animals of a desert must be able to survive extremes of temperature as well as the dryness.

Most desert plants have special ways of storing water. Cacti have fat, water-filled stems and thick skins to keep water in. Desert animals are also adapted to the dry conditions. Some, such as desert frogs, remain dormant until it rains, and then they breed and lay their eggs. The tadpoles develop into adult frogs in a few weeks.

Long legs raise a lizard off hot sand.

A screech owl nests in a hole in a cactus.

Arctic and tundra

There are few plants on the land in the Arctic and Antarctic, so all the animals that live there have to get their food from the sea. Single-celled photosynthesizers in the plankton at the topmost layer of the sea produce food that larger animals, such as fish, feed on. Seals and penguins eat fish, and predators such as polar bears eat seals.

The slightly warmer lands south of the Arctic support tundra vegetation, typically lichens, mosses and dwarf shrubs. The subsoil is permanently frozen, but in the summer there are lakes and boggy pools which provide ideal breeding grounds for flying insects such as mosquitoes. They help to provide food for the birds that migrate to the tundra by the millions to nest and rear chicks. As winter approaches, they fly south again to warmer climates.

A polar bear's thick, oily fur keeps out the cold.

Scrub

Scrub is any type of vegetation with small trees, bushes and low-growing plants adapted to dry, hot summers. Mediterranean scrub is a particular type found around the Mediterranean Sea. Small areas also occur in parts of Australia and California where the climate is similar. Nearer the equator there is another kind of scrub where the savanna blends with the seasonal forest. Insects are abundant in scrubland, and many animals feed on them, particularly lizards and insectivorous birds.

Unfertile scrubland in central Greece

Mountains

Mountain plants have to survive intense cold, especially at night, and thin soil that is easily swept away by rain and wind. Mountain animals face similar problems, as well as a lack of places to shelter. Wild goats and sheep are some of the most successful. They are remarkably sure-footed and can leap from one rocky crag to another in search of plants to eat. Some predators, such as foxes and wolves, move up into the mountains in summer, but retreat to the valleys in winter.

The bighorn sheep lives in high mountains.

Swamps and marshes

In swamps and marshes the ground is permanently waterlogged. Tall reeds are a common type of vegetation, and they provide an excellent home for many small mammals and birds, and a breeding ground for millions of insects. Birds of prey, such as the marsh harrier, fly low over the reeds, seeking out small animals and swooping down among the reeds to seize them in their talons. Other predators, such as herons and otters, feed off fish and frogs that thrive in the swampy water. Ducks and geese feed mainly on plants, and make their nests in the reeds.

In the tropics, swamps provide homes for turtles, terrapins, alligators and giant snakes such as the anaconda, which glides through the shallow water in search of prey.

Horses in the swamps of Camargue, France

Seashore life

Throughout the world there is a special sort of habitat where the land meets the sea. In the Northern Hemisphere, the shoreline may be sandy or rocky, with different types of plants and animals living on each. The influence of the tides, rising and falling twice a day, is very important. The lower shore is always covered with water except at the spring tides (twice a month). In the middle intertidal zone, plants and animals are covered by the sea twice a day, while the high intertidal zone has long dry periods during low tide. Above this there is the splash zone, wetted by only the highest tides. It has its own special animals and plants.

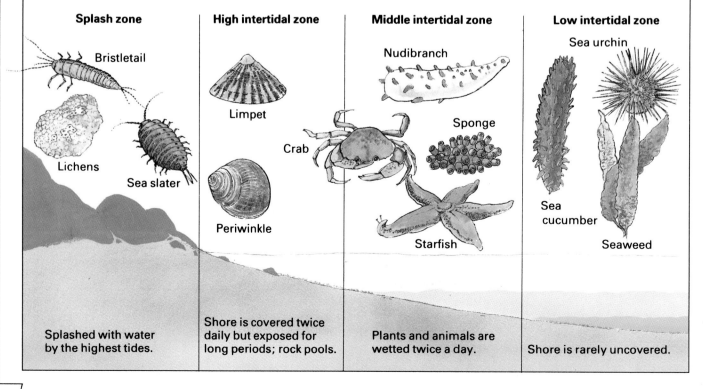

Splash zone
Bristletail
Lichens
Sea slater

High intertidal zone
Limpet
Crab
Periwinkle

Middle intertidal zone
Nudibranch
Sponge
Starfish

Low intertidal zone
Sea urchin
Sea cucumber
Seaweed

Splashed with water by the highest tides.

Shore is covered twice daily but exposed for long periods; rock pools.

Plants and animals are wetted twice a day.

Shore is rarely uncovered.

Forest and woodland

Trees are the natural vegetation of much of the Earth's land surface. Different types suit different climates, so there are several major forest zones (see map on page 141). The boreal forests of the north consist mainly of conifers, such as firs and pines, which are adapted to the harsh conditions. Snow slides off the downward slope of their branches, and their tough needles are not damaged by frost as thin leaves would be. By keeping their needles through winter, they are ready as soon as spring arrives to start photosynthesizing and to make best use of the short summer growing season. Farther south, in temperate regions, is a band of broadleaved forest. It is made up of deciduous trees such as oak and beech, which shed their leaves in autumn. The forests of the tropics are much richer in animal life, especially the tropical rainforest where there is constant growth and activity all the year round.

An ancient oak forest with moss-covered stones

Deforestation

People have been cutting down trees for thousands of years, ever since farming began in prehistoric times. Most of the deciduous forests of Europe were lost in this way. In the tropics, the rainforest had remained largely untouched until this century because the trees are so massive that they were difficult to clear before machines became available. Now even this forest is being felled and at the present rate there will soon be none left.

Destroying Amazon forest trees to make a road

Acid rain

Many forests in the Northern Hemisphere are now dying because of pollution. Gases such as sulfur dioxide released by burning coal and oil in power stations, and nitrogen oxides from car and truck exhaust enter the atmosphere and dissolve in rain to form acids. The acid rain falls on forests and lakes, affects the soil and water and kills the trees and fish. But because the forests and lakes are habitats for many animals, they too are affected and die.

German forest trees killed by acid rain

The biggest effect on the environment is caused by the growth of the human race. In the last hundred years, the world's population has increased from 1.5 billion to 5 billion. At the current rate of growth, by the year 2000 it will be about 6 billion and will begin to stabilize at about twice that figure by the 22nd century.

Ten thousand years ago, human beings lived by hunting and by gathering berries and nuts. Like other living things, they were part of a complicated food web, and their population remained fairly constant. Then people began farming and everything changed. People altered the ecosystem so that the food web produced more and more of the sort of food they could eat. The human population began to rise, and other animals were squeezed out.

In the present century this process has accelerated rapidly. World population is growing faster than ever. Scientists produce pesticides, which kill many living things (not just pests). Other chemicals pollute the soil, the rivers, seas and air – posing another major threat to life. Many biologists believe that the world could be approaching a major environmental crisis.

Preserving the habitat

There are now very few untouched natural habitats, such as coral reefs and tropical rainforests. It is important to preserve these areas because they provide a home for many animals and plants that cannot survive anywhere else. And once the habitats are destroyed, they cannot usually be recreated.

Even where there is farming, forestry or other human activity on the land, it is still possible for wildlife to survive. Traditional methods of farming tended to be better than modern ones, because the land was not used so intensively – there was still room for wild plants and animals. Returning to less intensive methods and reducing the use of pesticides would result in more wildlife.

Coral reefs are in danger from fishermen.

Under-road badger passage

Many animals are killed by road vehicles. Badgers and toads, which regularly cross roads at a particular place, can be helped by underpasses.

Oil pipelines

The natural appearance of the environment can be preserved by laying oil and gas pipelines, and electricity cables, underground.

The best form of conservation preserves and protects the existing natural environment. Measures can also be taken to restore land that has been spoiled by human activities.

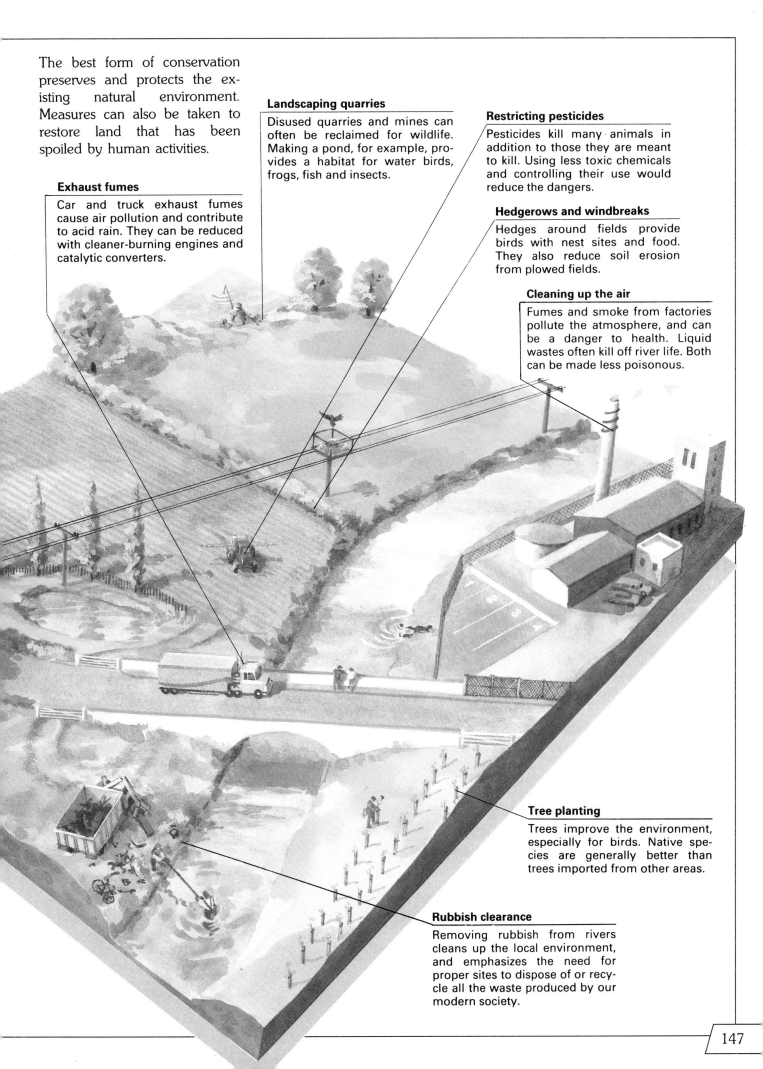

Landscaping quarries

Disused quarries and mines can often be reclaimed for wildlife. Making a pond, for example, provides a habitat for water birds, frogs, fish and insects.

Restricting pesticides

Pesticides kill many animals in addition to those they are meant to kill. Using less toxic chemicals and controlling their use would reduce the dangers.

Exhaust fumes

Car and truck exhaust fumes cause air pollution and contribute to acid rain. They can be reduced with cleaner-burning engines and catalytic converters.

Hedgerows and windbreaks

Hedges around fields provide birds with nest sites and food. They also reduce soil erosion from plowed fields.

Cleaning up the air

Fumes and smoke from factories pollute the atmosphere, and can be a danger to health. Liquid wastes often kill off river life. Both can be made less poisonous.

Tree planting

Trees improve the environment, especially for birds. Native species are generally better than trees imported from other areas.

Rubbish clearance

Removing rubbish from rivers cleans up the local environment, and emphasizes the need for proper sites to dispose of or recycle all the waste produced by our modern society.

CLASSIFICATION CHART

The variety of living things is enormous. Plants, for example, range from microscopic mosses to conifer trees growing 100m (330ft) tall. Yet all plants photosynthesize and, in terms of internal structure and methods of reproduction, can be grouped into just four main sub-divisions. The most primitive plants are the Bryophytes. These lack true roots, stems or leaves. The next sub-division, the Pteridophytes, includes plants with roots, stems and leaves but which depend on water for their sexual reproduction. Third are the Gymnosperms, the cone-forming plants, and last, the Angiosperms, the flowering plants.

Algae, fungi, lichens and bacteria are often treated as simple types of plants. They each have one or more plant characteristics. In the main part of the book this treatment is maintained to highlight the probable course of evolution of today's plants. It shows that the first plants were probably single-celled aquatic organisms and what adaptations were needed to become large, land-living organisms such as conifer trees. Biologists, though, now often classify these organisms separately. Viruses are considered by some scientists as non-living things and by others as living, so are kept separate.

PLANT KINGDOM				
Gymnosperms	Bryophytes	Pteridophytes	Angiosperms	
			Monocotyledons	Dicotyledons

Gymnosperms: Conifers, Ginkgoes, Yews
Bryophytes: Mosses, Liverworts
Pteridophytes: Horsetails, Clubmosses, Ferns
Angiosperms — Monocotyledons: Palms, Grasses, Orchids, Lilies, Irises, Bamboos
Angiosperms — Dicotyledons: Broadleaf trees, Shrubs, Herbaceous plants

ORGANISMS SOMETIMES CLASSED AS PLANTS			
Algae	Bacteria	Lichens	Fungi

Algae: Euglena, Spirogyra, Plant plankton, Seaweed
Bacteria: Bacteria
Lichens: Lichens
Fungi: Molds, Yeasts, Puffballs, Toadstools

VIRUSES

CLASSIFICATION CHART

There are two major divisions within the Animal Kingdom – backboned animals, the vertebrates, which include fish, amphibians and mammals, and animals that lack a backbone, the invertebrates, with which this book deals. The most primitive of the invertebrates, the Protozoans, represent the first type of animals to evolve on Earth more than 3 billion years ago.

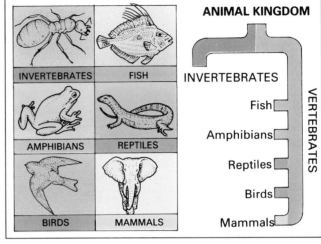

ANIMAL KINGDOM

INVERTEBRATES	FISH
AMPHIBIANS	REPTILES
BIRDS	MAMMALS

INVERTEBRATES

VERTEBRATES
Fish
Amphibians
Reptiles
Birds
Mammals

SEGMENTED WORMS

Bristleworms	Earthworms	Leeches

ARTHROPODS

Pauropods	Millipedes	Centipedes	Symphylans	Springtails	Two-pronged bristletails	Three-pronged bristletails

ARTHROPODS (continued)

Insects	Arachnids	Crustaceans	King crabs	Velvet worms	Proturans

MESOZOANS

COMB JELLIES

Insects	Arachnids	Crustaceans
Mayflies Dragonflies Notopterans Stoneflies Web-spinners Cockroaches Mantises Termites Zorapterans Grasshoppers Stick insects Earwigs Book-lice Bird-lice Sucking lice Thrips Bugs Lacewings Alderflies Snakeflies Beetles Strepsipterans Scorpionflies Caddis flies Zeuglopterans Butterflies and moths True flies Fleas Ants, bees, wasps	Scorpions Pseudoscorpions Camel spiders Micro-whip scorpions Whip scorpions Amblypygids Spiders Ricinuleids Harvestmen Mites and ticks	Cephalocarids Branchiopods Mussel shrimps Copepods Mystacocarids Fish lice Barnacles Prawns, crabs, lobsters

SPONGES

Calcareous sponges	Glass sponges	Horny sponges

FLATWORMS

Free-living	Flukes	Tapeworms

RIBBON WORMS

ENTOPROCTS

THORNY-HEADED WORMS

HEMICHORDATES

Acorn worms	Pterobranchs

COELENTERATES

Hydrozoans	Jellyfish	Sea anemones and corals

PHORONID WORMS

PROTOZOA

Flagellates	Sarcodines	Spore-formers	Ciliates

BEARD BEARERS

SEA SPIDERS

MOSS ANIMALS

LAMP SHELLS

ECHINODERMS

Starfish	Brittlestars	Sea urchins	Sea cucumbers	Sea lilies

PEANUT WORMS

ECHIUROID WORMS

MOLLUSKS

Monoplacophorans	Chitons	Snails and slugs	Tusk shells	Bivalve molluscs	Squid, cuttlefish, octopuses

TONGUE WORMS

ASCHELMINTHES

Rotifers	Gastrotrichs	Kinorhynchs	Priapulids	Horsehair worms	Roundworms

WATER BEARS

ARROW WORMS

N.B. Tunicates, such as sea squirts and lancelets, form a link between vertebrates and invertebrates.

CLASSIFICATION CHARTS

Animals with backbones are called vertebrates. There are only about 40,000 different sorts of vertebrates, but because their bodies are supported with an internal skeleton they can grow to be much bigger than invertebrates. Some large invertebrates live in water, but on land almost all animals with backbones are bigger. The vertebrates are divided into five classes. These are the fishes, the amphibians, the reptiles, the mammals and the birds. On these two pages you can see some of the main groups, called orders, within the classes. Fishes, which first evolved over 400 million years ago, breath through gills and live in water. Amphibians, which evolved from fishes about 280 million years ago start their life in water, but lose their

FISH						
Bony Fish				**Cartiliginous fish**		**Jawless fish**
RAY FINNED FISH			FLESHY FINNED FISH	CHIMAERAS	SHARKS AND RAYS	
Teleosts	Garpikes and Bowfins	Birchiris and Sturgeons				

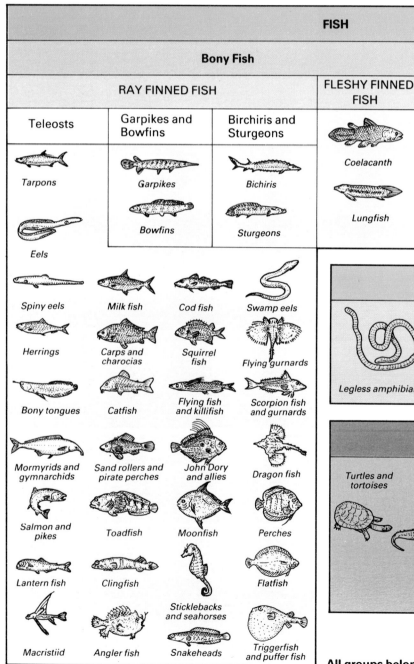

Teleosts: Tarpons, Eels, Spiny eels, Herrings, Bony tongues, Mormyrids and gymnarchids, Salmon and pikes, Lantern fish, Macristiid, Milk fish, Carps and charocias, Catfish, Sand rollers and pirate perches, Toadfish, Clingfish, Angler fish, Cod fish, Squirrel fish, Flying fish and killifish, John Dory and allies, Moonfish, Seahorses, Sticklebacks and seahorses, Snakeheads, Swamp eels, Flying gurnards, Scorpion fish and gurnards, Dragon fish, Perches, Flatfish, Triggerfish and puffer fish

Garpikes and Bowfins: Garpikes, Bowfins

Birchiris and Sturgeons: Bichiris, Sturgeons

Fleshy finned fish: Coelacanth, Lungfish

Chimaeras: Chimaeras

Sharks and Rays: Sharks, Skates and Rays

Jawless fish: Hagfish and Lampreys

AMPHIBIANS

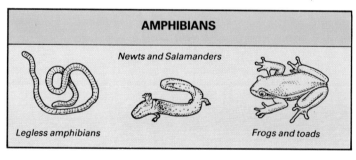

Newts and Salamanders

Legless amphibians   Frogs and toads

REPTILES

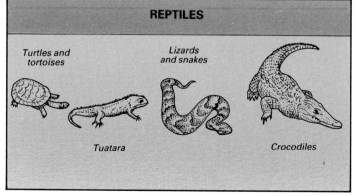

Turtles and tortoises   Lizards and snakes

Tuatara   Crocodiles

All groups belong to vertebrates

gills and are able to colonise the land, although they must in most cases keep their bodies moist. Reptiles breathe air, have a waterproof skin and lay shelled eggs so they are able to live their lives on land. But they are cold-blooded so they are restricted to the warmer parts of the world. Mammals are warm-blooded and insulated with fur or fat, so they are able to live and be active in cold as well as warm places. Most mammal babies are protected inside their mothers' bodies until they are ready to be born. Then they are fed on milk. The first birds lived about 150 million years ago. Because they can fly they can travel to parts of the world that mammals cannot reach easily. Like mammals they are warm-blooded, but they are insulated with feathers which are an even better protection than fur.

BIRDS

Kiwis

Ostrich

Rheas

Cassowaries and emu

Tinamous

Grebes

Divers and loons

Penguins

Albatrosses, shearwaters, petrels

Pelicans and relatives

Herons, storks, flamingoes

Screamers and ducks

Eagles, hawks, falcons

Game birds and hoatzin

Cranes and relatives

Waders, gulls, auks

Pigeons and sandgrouse

Parrots, macaws

Cuckoos and turacos

Owls

Frogmouths and nighjars

Swifts and hummingbirds

Trogons

Mousebirds

Kingfishers, hornbills

Woodpeckers, toucans

Perching birds

MAMMALS

Marsupials and placentals		Monotremes
PLACENTALS	MARSUPIALS	

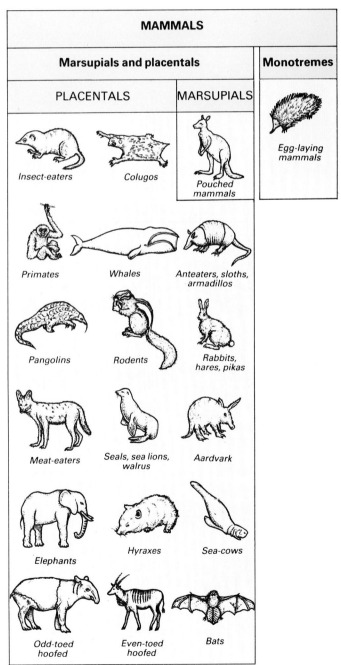

Insect-eaters

Colugos

Pouched mammals

Egg-laying mammals

Primates

Whales

Anteaters, sloths, armadillos

Pangolins

Rodents

Rabbits, hares, pikas

Meat-eaters

Seals, sea lions, walrus

Aardvark

Elephants

Hyraxes

Sea-cows

Odd-toed hoofed

Even-toed hoofed

Bats

EVOLUTIONARY TIME CHART

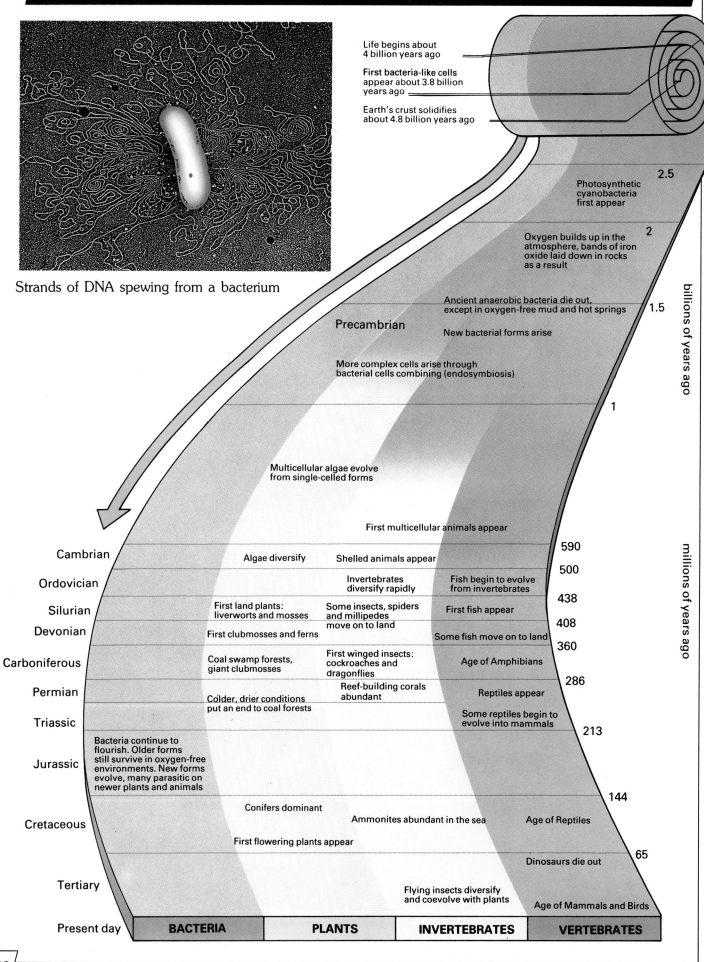

Strands of DNA spewing from a bacterium

Life begins about 4 billion years ago

First bacteria-like cells appear about 3.8 billion years ago

Earth's crust solidifies about 4.8 billion years ago

Photosynthetic cyanobacteria first appear — 2.5

Oxygen builds up in the atmosphere, bands of iron oxide laid down in rocks as a result — 2

Ancient anaerobic bacteria die out, except in oxygen-free mud and hot springs — 1.5

Precambrian

New bacterial forms arise

More complex cells arise through bacterial cells combining (endosymbiosis) — 1

Multicellular algae evolve from single-celled forms

First multicellular animals appear

Period	Bacteria/Plants	Plants/Invertebrates	Vertebrates	Mya
Cambrian	Algae diversify	Shelled animals appear		590
Ordovician		Invertebrates diversify rapidly	Fish begin to evolve from invertebrates	500
Silurian	First land plants: liverworts and mosses	Some insects, spiders and millipedes move on to land	First fish appear	438
Devonian	First clubmosses and ferns		Some fish move on to land	408
Carboniferous	Coal swamp forests, giant clubmosses	First winged insects: cockroaches and dragonflies	Age of Amphibians	360
Permian	Colder, drier conditions put an end to coal forests	Reef-building corals abundant	Reptiles appear	286
Triassic			Some reptiles begin to evolve into mammals	213
Jurassic	Bacteria continue to flourish. Older forms still survive in oxygen-free environments. New forms evolve, many parasitic on newer plants and animals			144
Cretaceous	Conifers dominant / First flowering plants appear	Ammonites abundant in the sea	Age of Reptiles	65
Tertiary		Flying insects diversify and coevolve with plants	Dinosaurs die out / Age of Mammals and Birds	
Present day	BACTERIA	PLANTS / INVERTEBRATES	VERTEBRATES	

billions of years ago

millions of years ago

EXTINCTION CHART

Extinction is a necessary part of evolution – it has been happening since life on Earth began. But today it is people who are responsible for most extinctions, and the rate has accelerated enormously during this century. Most has been caused by hunting and the destruction of habitats. Many mammals and birds have disappeared, and a great many more are endangered. There are also a large number of reptiles, amphibians and fish – and thousands of species of plants and insects – that die out every year. The tropical rainforests are a major area of loss, partly because it has such a tremendous variety of wildlife and partly because it is being destroyed at such a fast rate.

Humpback whales are in danger of extinction.

1 Mammoth
2 Woolly rhinoceros
3 Cave lion
4 Cave bear
5 Irish elk
6 American mastodon
7 Imperial mammoth
8 Great ground sloth
9 Saber-tooth tiger
10 Dire wolf
11 Reunion solitaire
12 Dodo
13 Guadaloupe amazon
14 Elephant bird
15 Aurochs
16 Steller's sea cow
17 Blue buck
18 Hispaniolan hutia
19 Green-and-yellow macaw
20 Moa
21 Dwarf emu
22 Rodriquez little owl
23 Sandwich rail
24 Great auk
25 Spectacled cormorant
26 Atlas bear
27 Tarpan
28 Sea mink
29 Portuguese ibex
30 Quagga
31 Warrah
32 Palestine painted frog
33 Abingdon Island tortoise

34 Round Island boa
35 Passenger pigeon
36 Carolina parakeet
37 Pink-headed duck
38 Lord Howe Island white-eye
39 Hawaiian O-O
40 Madagascar serpent eagle
41 Kauai Nukupuu
42 Greater rabbit bandicoot
43 Arizona jaguar
44 Schomburgk's deer

45 Caribbean monk seal
46 Thylacine
47 Jamaican long-tongued bat
48 Barbary lion
49 Newfoundland white wolf
50 Bali tiger
51 Italian spade-footed toad
52 Chinese alligator
53 Central Asian cobra
54 Geometric tortoise
55 Hawksbill turtle

56 Japanese crested ibis
57 California condor
58 Red-billed curassow
59 Black robin
60 Reunion petrel
61 Abbott's booby
62 Hawaiian gallinule
63 Mauritius pink pigeon
64 Western ground parrot
65 Hawaiian crow
66 Leadbeater's opossum
67 Ghost bat
68 Woolly spider monkey
69 Mountain gorilla
70 Blue whale
71 Humpback whale
72 Indus dolphin
73 Northern kit fox
74 Baluchistan bear
75 Giant otter
76 Siberian tiger
77 Asiatic lion
78 Mediterranean monk seal
79 Grevy's zebra
80 Przewalski's horse
81 Mountain tapir
82 Great Indian rhinoceros
83 Swamp deer
84 Giant sable antelope
85 Indri
86 Orangutan
87 Sumatran rhinoceros
88 Mountain anoa

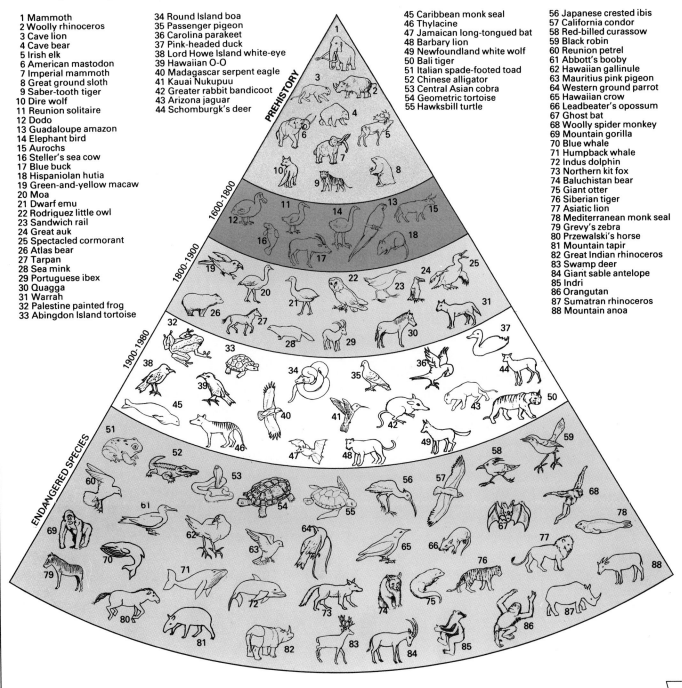

PREHISTORY
1600-1800
1800-1900
1900-1980
ENDANGERED SPECIES

GLOSSARY

abdomen the rear part of an insect's body which contains the internal organs of digestion, excretion and reproduction.

adaptation a feature or behavior that allows an animal to live in a particular environment or feed on a specific food.

algae simple plants or plant-like photosynthesizing organisms consisting of either a single cell or many cells not organized into leaves, stems, and roots.

airfoil the name given to the shape of bird wings and aircraft, which are curved on top and flap together.

amino acids chief components of proteins.

anther the male part of a flower, which produces pollen.

antheridium the male reproductive organ of lower plants.

aquatic an animal or plant which lives in water.

archegonium the female reproductive organ of lower plants.

artery a blood vessel that carries blood from the heart to the body tissues and organs.

asexual reproduction method of producing offspring that does not involve the joining of a male's sperm and female's egg, as in binary fission - the simple division of the animal into two identical individuals – or budding – in which a bud or offshoot develops into a new individual.

bacteria single-celled plant-like organisms, some of which cause diseases of animals and plants, others the decomposition of dead organisms.

binary fission a method of asexual reproduction among some single-celled organisms involving division of the cell in two identical daughter cells.

bone hard material forming skeleton of most vertebrates. There are about 206 bones in an adult human skeleton.

bract a leaf on a flower stalk, specialized to protect a flower.

brain the co-ordination and control center of an animal's nervous system.

budding see asexual reproduction.

capillary narrow, thin-walled blood vessel that permits oxygen, carbon dioxide, and food materials to pass between cells of the body and the bloodstream.

cambrium a layer of actively growing cells inside a stem.

camouflage patterns, colors and shapes on an insect's body which blend in with the background, so it is difficult to see.

carbon dioxide gas found in the Earth's atmosphere. It is used by plants to make food; they combine carbon dioxide with water to make a molecule of sugar. Carbon dioxide is produced when plants and animals break down food to yield.

carnivore a meat eating animal.

carrion dead, rotting flesh.

cartilaginous fish whose skeleton is composed of cartilage – elastic tissue.

cell the smallest unit or building block of living things. Different types of cells have different jobs – for example, nerve, muscle, blood cells – but all work in the same way.

cephalothorax the front part of some arthropods, consisting of the head and thorax sections joined together.

chlorophyll a green pigment inside plant cells that can trap sunlight and use its energy to make simple chemicals into complex energy-storing ones. It is the site of the first stage of photosynthesis.

cilia tiny hairs covering the cell surface of some protozoans and other invertebrates, used for feeding or movement.

cold-blooded an animal whose body temperature depends upon the temperature of its environment, as in fishes.

community all the living organisms within a particular area.

cotyledon a specialized food storing leaf within a seed.

crustaceans arthropods with a tough exoskeleton armour, a cephalothorax and paired limbs or appendages on all body segments, for example crabs, lobsters, crayfish, prawns.

decomposers organisms that feed on the remains of living things, or on the waste products they produce (e.g. cow dung). In feeding on these items, decomposers provide a valuable service in removing them and in returning the nutrients they contain to the soil or water. The major decomposers include dung beetles and vultures.

deoxygenated blood low in oxygen but high in carbon dioxide content. Carbon dioxide is a waste product of animal chemistry and must be eliminated from the body.

disperse to spread spores or seeds away from the parent plant to prevent overcrowding.

DNA deoxyribonucleic acid, the hereditary material that makes up genes.

dormant a period of time during which a plant rests and makes little or no new growth.

ecosystem all the living organisms in a particular region, as well as the soil, water and other non-living features that interact with them.

egg female reproductive cell with its own provision of food for the growing embryo. The egg must be fertilized by the male sperm before development of the embryo can begin.

embryo an early stage in development of an animal – from the female's fertilized egg until the young hatches.

environment the conditions in which an organism lives.

enzyme special chemicals which help chemical reactions to take place.

epidermis a protective layer of cells on the outside of a leaf or stem.

evolution a very slow process by which new species arise as a result of changes that occur in population of animals or plants.

exoskeleton hard outer covering of arthropods that functions as an external skeleton.

extinction the complete dying out of a species.

fertilization the fusing together of male and female reproductive cells (sperm and egg) to form an embryo.

flock a large or small group of birds that flies together. Many birds migrate in large flocks, often with more than one species.

frond the leaf-like structure of large algae such as seaweeds or the usually finely divided leaves of ferns.

fungi organisms with some plant-like features but which do not photosynthesize.

gall a swelling made by some plants when attacked by insects such as tiny wasps.

gamete a reproductive cell such as sperm or egg. Sexual reproduction involves fertilization, the fusion of male and female gametes.

gametophyte a stage in the life cycle of plants which produces gametes.

germination the sprouting of a new plant from a seed or spore.

gills feathery breathing organs of animals that live in water – the equivalent of lungs in land-living animals.

habitat a place where an animal or plant lives such as a forest, desert or sea.

heart muscular pumping organ that sends blood to all parts of the body.

GLOSSARY

herbivore an animal that feeds on plant material.

hermaphrodite animal with both male and female reproductive organs.

host creature on or in which a parasite lives.

invertebrate animal that lacks a backbone. Invertebrates include many aquatic creatures, such as jellyfish, sponges and starfish, but insects form the largest group.

larva young, immature stage in the life cycle of many animals. It is usually very different in appearance from the adult and cannot reproduce.

lifestyle the way of life of an animal, including what and how it eats, where it lives, and how it breeds.

locomotion method of movement from one place to another, such as running, swimming and jumping.

mature describing the stage at which an animal is sufficiently well developed to be able to reproduce.

metamorphosis the transformation of a young insect to an adult.

migration the movement of animals from one place to another, usually on a seasonal basis.

nerve cord another name for the spinal cord. The notochord is the forerunner of the backbone.

nervous system/nerves special body structure(s) able to send, receive and, as the brain, interpret information in the form of electrical messages (known as nerve impulses).

nocturnal birds that are active mainly at night, such as owls. Nocturnal birds have special ways of finding their food and their way in the dark.

nucleus the control center of a cell. It controls the genetic material DNA.

organ major part of an animal or plant which has a specific job, for instance the heart, brain and lungs. Organs are made up of different types of tissues, which are themselves composed of various cells.

organism a living thing such as an animal or plant.

ovule part of a flower containing the female gamete that will develop into a seed.

ovum an unfertilized egg.

oxygen gas that makes up 20 percent of the Earth's atmosphere. Most living organisms cannot live without oxygen, and use it to break down food and release energy from it.

oxygenated blood rich in oxygen.

parasite an organism that lives in or on another creature from which it gets its food (the host). A parasite may eventually kill its food source.

pesticides chemicals used to kill off unwanted organisms.

photosynthesis the production of food by green plants from carbon dioxide and water using sunlight as energy.

placenta an organ, which during pregnancy of certain mammals, grows within the womb and which transports oxygen, food and waste materials between the mother's and the embryo's blood system.

plankton tiny animals and plants that float in surface waters of seas, lakes and ponds and form the main food of many larger animals; they include the larvae of many invertebrates.

pollen fine powder-like material containing the male gametes of flowering plants.

pollution release of unwanted or dangerous materials into the natural environment. Some pollution is caused by natural forces, such as volcanoes that throw out ash and lava. But most pollution results from human activities, such as the spraying of crops with pesticides.

population all the members of a given species of plants or animals that live within a particular area. The members of a population can interbreed freely, so there is an unrestricted flow of genes within the population.

predator an animal which gets its food by hunting and killing other animals.

prey an animal which is hunted, killed and eaten by another animal.

prehensile able to seize or grasp.

primitive an animal that resembles its distant ancestors, not one that is simple in structure or underdeveloped.

pupa the chrysalis stage, between the larva and the adult, in insects such as flies and butterflies, used to suck up liquid food.

reproduction process of producing offspring. It usually involves the male fertilizing the female's egg with sperm.

savanna the dry grasslands of East Africa.

scavenger an animal that eats dead or dying animals.

sexual reproduction production of new plants by the fusion of male and female gametes, either sperm and egg or pollen grain and egg within an ovule.

skull box-like skeleton of the head composed of many bones fused together and providing protection for the brain and sense organs, such as the eyes.

sloughing the process by which snakes and some species of lizards moult or shed the outer layer of skin at once, rather than gradually, as most animals do.

species animals or plants that have the same structure and that are capable of reproducing together. Smallest group commonly used in biological classification.

sperm the male's reproductive cells, containing genetic material. In sexual reproduction sperm must fertilize the female's eggs for offspring to be reproduced.

spinal cord extension of the brain running the length of the body and enclosed within a canal in the vertebral column or backbone. Nerves radiate out from the spinal cord to reach all parts of the body.

spore an asexual reproductive or resting structure from which new individuals develop.

sporophyte a stage in the life cycle of plants that reproduces spores.

startle colors bright colors on an animal's body that are usually hidden but which can be revealed to surprise an enemy and ward off attack

stereoscopic vision two slightly different views, each provided by one eye, that combine into one solid picture.

symbiosis close relationship between two different organisms. There are several forms of symbiosis, including mutualism and commensalism. (Some scientists use symbiosis in a different way, to mean only those relationships in which both species benefit).

territory area of land occupied by an individual or group of animals, the boundaries of which they define using scent and which they defend, often with aggressive displays.

thorax the middle part of an insect's body, to which the wings and legs are attached. In vertebrates, the region of the body that contains the heart and lungs.

vascular system the water conducting vessels and food-transporting sieve tubes within more advanced plants such as ferns, conifers and flowering plants.

vegetation the type of plants that grow in an area – for example mostly trees in forests and woods and grasses in savannahs.

vein blood vessel carrying blood from body to heart.

vertebral column another name for the backbone. It consists of many bony units linked together to form a flexible stiffening rod the length of the body.

vertebrate animal with a backbone. Vertebrates include fish, amphibians, reptiles, birds and mammals.

warm-blooded an animal whose internal body temperature stays constant whatever the temperature outside, so it can remain active in warm or cold weather.

INDEX

Photographic Credits

Ardea; Bruce Coleman; Linda Gamlin; Robert Harding Library; Hutchinson Library; NHPA; Photosource; Planet Earth; Science Photo Library; Seaphot; Spectrum; Survival Anglia; Zefa.